# REVISE 11+

G000252677

# English
## Ten-Minute Tests

Series Consultant: Harry Smith
Author: David Grant

**THE REVISE 11⁺ SERIES**

For the full range of Pearson Revise 11⁺ titles visit:
www.pearsonschools.co.uk/revise11plus

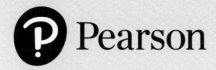

Pearson

# Contents

## How to use this book

Each test corresponds to a practice section in one of the two Revise 11+ English Practice Books.

Work through the practice sections, then have a go at the corresponding Ten-Minute Test.

You could also work through the tests in order, or focus on the skills you know you need more practice in first.

Spend 10 minutes on each test and use the answers in the back of the book to mark your work.

# 1 Parts of speech

In this test you will practise identifying and using different parts of speech. These could include:
- words such as nouns, verbs, adjectives and adverbs
- phrases such as noun phrases, adverbial phrases and adjectival phrases.

**10**

**1** Circle the verb in the sentence below.

We (went) on holiday for two weeks.

**1 mark**

**2** Underline the adjective in the sentence below and complete the sentence with an adverb.

We had to sit in a hot car for hours as the traffic was moving very _slowly_ .

**2 marks**

**3** Circle the **two** verbs in the sentence below.

I (love) football although I hardly ever (watch) it on the television.

**2 marks**

**4** What are modal verbs used for? Tick **one** box.

☐ to express an action or a state of being

☑ to express how likely or necessary something is

☐ to describe a verb

☐ to describe a noun

**1 mark**

**5** Which word below is not an adjective? Circle **one** answer.

shiny        wooden        large        (box)        heavy

**1 mark**

**6** Complete the sentence below by adding **one** appropriate adjective and **one** appropriate adverb.

Swans are _beautiful_ because they swim so _gracefully_ .

**2 marks**

**7** Which word below is not an adverb? Circle **one** answer.

quickly        silly        suddenly        amazingly        (often)

**1 mark**

**8** What part of speech is the bold word in the sentence below? Write your answer below.

You **must** never talk to strangers.

__instruction modal verb__

**1 mark**

**9** What part of speech is the phrase below? Tick **one** box.

after two or three hours

☐ noun phrase

☑ adverbial phrase

☐ adjectival phrase

☐ verb phrase

**1 mark**

1

**10** Complete the sentence below, using a modal verb.

> 1 mark

Because electricity is very dangerous, _____ _____ ✗

_____ .

**11** Complete the sentence below, using an adjective and an adverb.

> 2 marks

Pigs are _pink and move slowly._ ✓✓

_____ .

**12** Is the statement below true or false? Tick **one** box.

> 1 mark

A noun phrase is a noun and any other words that are near it.

☑ true ✗

☐ false

**13** Underline the noun phrases in the sentence below.

> 2 marks

As I watched from <u>my hiding place</u>, ✓ a tall, dark, <u>shadowy figure</u> ✓ appeared as if from nowhere.

**14** Complete the sentence below, using a noun phrase.

> 1 mark ?

_Rainy days_ are never very enjoyable. ✓

**15** Underline the adjectival phrase in the sentence below.

> 1 mark

My dog is <u>extremely naughty.</u> ✓

**16** Which phrase below is an adjectival phrase? Tick **one** box.

> 1 mark

☐ running quickly to school

☑ small, blue, smelly ✓

☐ after several months

☐ on a stormy night in November

### Time to reflect

**Mark your test out of 21. How did you do?**

Check your answers in the back of the book. If any of your answers are incorrect, go to practice section 1 in Practice Book 1 to revise this topic.

15/21

# 2 Tenses

In this test you will practise identifying and using tenses.

**10**

**1**  Which words or phrases in the sentence below tell you what tense it is in? Circle your answers.

I (kicked) the ball through a window and (smashed) it into tiny pieces.

**2 marks**

**2**  Which tense is used to talk about something that has already happened? Tick **one** box.

☐ present

☐ present progressive

☑ past

☐ future

**1 mark**

**3**  Underline the correct word in brackets to complete each sentence below.

**a**  I (buy / bought / have bought) a new game last week.

**b**  I (am saving / have saved / will save) up for a new game at the moment.

**c**  I (buy / will buy / have bought) it as soon as I have saved enough.

**3 marks**

**4**  Underline the correct word in brackets to complete each sentence below.

**a**  My best friend (is called / will call / called) Meera.

**b**  Last weekend we (go / went / will have gone) ice skating for her birthday.

**c**  In the summer I (am going / went / is going) on a camping holiday with her family.

**3 marks**

**5**  Underline **three** examples of the present perfect tense in the sentence below.

Ever since I was a baby, we have visited my grandparents every summer. I look forward to it every year, especially as it means that school has finished and the summer holidays have arrived!

**3 marks**

**6**  How can you recognise the present progressive tense? Tick **one** box.

☐ Look for a form of the verb 'to have' plus a past tense verb.

☐ Look for the verb 'will' or 'shall'.

☐ Look for an adverb.

☑ Look for a form of the verb 'to be' plus main verbs ending in -ing.

**1 mark**

**7**  Circle the verb in the present progressive tense in the sentence below.

I am taking up (running) because I want to be healthier.

**1 mark**

**8** Rewrite the sentence below in the present perfect tense.

Kam tries on a new pair of trainers and decides to buy them.  ✗

1 mark

_____

_____

**9** Draw lines to match each sentence below with its correct tense.

I am waiting for a bus.  → present perfect ✓

I waited thirty minutes for a bus.  → present progressive ✓

I have waited ages for a bus.  → simple past ✓

3 marks

**10** Complete the sentences below using verbs in the appropriate tense.

I always ___do___ the same thing every day. When I ___get___ ✗ home, I always

___do___ ✓ my homework straight away. When I ___finish___ all of my homework,

I ___get___ to watch television. ✓

5 marks

**11** Which sentence below is written in the present tense? Tick **one** box.

☐ I am often late for school.

☐ I shall make sure I get to school on time.

☑ I'll go to bed at a sensible time. ✗

☐ I will get up ten minutes early.

1 mark

**12** Which sentence below is written in the future perfect tense? Tick **one** box.

☑ I am going to London next week.

☐ We are going to go on the London Eye.

☐ I will be pleased when we are back on solid ground. ✗

☐ I will have overcome my fear of heights.

1 mark

2/5

## Time to reflect

### Mark your test out of 25. How did you do?

Check your answers in the back of the book. If any of your answers are incorrect, go to practice section 2 in Practice Book 1 to revise this topic.

# 3 Common punctuation marks

In this test you will practise using a range of punctuation marks accurately.

**⏱ 10**

**1**   Which of the words below does not always need a capital letter? Tick **one** box.

☐ I

☐ England

☐ Arthur

☐ We

**1 mark**

**2**   In which section is the punctuation mistake? Circle the correct number.

The first time / I went to london, / I got very lost.
      1              2              3

**1 mark**

**3**   Underline **five** words in the sentence below that should begin with a capital letter.

last april we went on holiday to an island called tenerife. it was great because the sun was shining and i went swimming every day.

**5 marks**

**4**   Is the statement below true or false? Tick **one** box.

If a sentence needs an answer, it should end with an exclamation mark.

☐ true

☐ false

**1 mark**

**5**   Rewrite the sentence below, using the correct punctuation.

Where are your socks Rafiq!

_____

**1 mark**

**6**   Which of the sentences below is punctuated correctly? Tick **one** box.

☐ Is there time to watch a film or do I have to go to bed.

☐ It has been raining for hours.

☐ I can't believe you just said that?

☐ I went to gymnastics club and I quite liked it

**1 mark**

**7**   Is the statement below true or false? Tick **one** box.

Commas should be used to separate words or phrases in a sentence that contain extra information.

☐ true

☐ false

**1 mark**

**8** Which of the sentences below is punctuated correctly? Tick **one** box.

☐ Hundreds of animal species are endangered, mainly due to the activities of humans.

☐ Tigers are an endangered species, there are only 4000 left in the wild.

☐ Elephants are hunted for their tusks. Even though it is illegal.

☐ There are only 700 mountain gorillas living in the wild

**1 mark**

**9** Rewrite the sentence below, adding the missing commas.

Being a successful athlete takes great skill hard work a lot of determination and a huge amount of time.

_____

_____

_____

**1 mark**

**10** Complete the sentence below, using the correct punctuation.

My three favourite pizza toppings are _____ .

**1 mark**

**11** Rewrite the information below in **one** sentence.

Steph got up at 7am. She washed her face. She cleaned her teeth. She went downstairs. She ate her breakfast.

_____

_____

_____

**1 mark**

**12** In which section is the punctuation mistake? Circle the correct number.

Mum sometimes makes a cooked lunch on sundays / but we often just have / sandwiches, crisps and fruit.

    1                                2                                3

**1 mark**

---

**Time to reflect**

**Mark your test out of 16. How did you do?**

Check your answers in the back of the book. If any of your answers are incorrect, go to practice section 3 in Practice Book 1 to revise this topic.

# 4 Sentences

In this test you will practise identifying and using the key features of sentences.

**10**

**1** Draw lines to match each word below to its correct meaning.

subject             the action described in the sentence

verb                the person or thing doing the action

object             the person or thing that has the action done to it

**3**
marks

**2** Label the subject, verb and object in the sentence below.

The police chased the burglar through the city.

**3**
marks

**3** Underline the mistake in each of the sentences below.

**a** He were very late for school this morning.

**b** I was asleep when you ring me.

**c** They was really upset because their team lost in the final.

**3**
marks

**4** Complete the sentences below by underlining the correct verbs in brackets.

**a** Kangaroos (live / lives) in Australia.

**b** The crowd (cheer / cheers) when a goal is scored.

**c** Nobody (know / knows) when it will happen again.

**3**
marks

**5** Which main clause completes the sentence below? Tick **one** box.

Although I love sweets, _____

☐ I try not to eat too many of them.      ☐ I always spend my allowance on them.

☐ because they are bad for your teeth.      ☐ I love chocolate.

**1**
mark

**6** Which sentence below is in the passive voice? Tick **one** box.

☐ My brother cooked dinner and, surprisingly, it was delicious.

☐ Dinner was cooked by my brother and, surprisingly, it was delicious.

☐ My brother cooked dinner and it was surprisingly delicious.

☐ Dinner cooked my brother and, surprisingly, it was delicious.

**1**
mark

**7** Rewrite the sentences below in the passive voice.

**a** I won first prize.

_____

**b** The sponsored swim raised a total of six hundred pounds.

_____

**2**
marks

7

**8** Underline the relative pronouns in the sentences below.

    **a** The team that I play for loses more matches than it wins.

    **b** The teacher, whose name was Ms Sweet, frowned angrily.

    **c** My mum, who has not ridden a bike for years, has started cycling to work.

<table><tr><td>3<br>marks</td></tr></table>

**9** Complete the sentence below, using a relative clause.

    She loved the present _____

    _____ .

<table><tr><td>1<br>mark</td></tr></table>

**10** Underline the subordinate clause in each of the sentences below.

    **a** Because we left him on his own, our dog chewed a hole in the sofa.

    **b** My mum was furious when she came home.

    **c** I'm not sure what she will do if he does it again.

<table><tr><td>3<br>marks</td></tr></table>

**11** Rewrite the sentences below, linking them together to form one complex sentence.

    I had to make a speech in front of the whole class. I was terrified.

    _____

    _____

    _____

<table><tr><td>1<br>mark</td></tr></table>

**12** Why is the sentence below incorrect? Tick **one** box.

    The kitchen worktop was covered in puddles of cake mixture who were dripping onto the floor.

    ☐ The passive voice is used incorrectly.

    ☐ The subject and verb do not agree.

    ☐ The main clause and subordinate clause do not match.

    ☐ The relative pronoun is used incorrectly.

<table><tr><td>1<br>mark</td></tr></table>

**Time to reflect**

**Mark your test out of 25. How did you do?**

Check your answers in the back of the book. If any of your answers are incorrect, go to practice section 4 in Practice Book 1 to revise this topic.

# 5 Parenthesis

In this test you will practise using commas, dashes and brackets to mark out additional information in a sentence.

**1**  Which sentence below uses parenthesis? Tick **one** box.

⬜ King Harold was defeated at the Battle of Hastings (which famously took place in 1066).

⬜ William the Conqueror's reign had a huge impact on England, some of which we still feel today.

⬜ The Bayeux Tapestry depicts the events leading up to the Norman invasion and the Battle of Hastings.

⬜ The tapestry is actually an embroidery and can still be seen in Bayeux today.

**1 mark**

**2**  Underline the parenthesis in the sentences below.

**a**  When I was very young (I was probably about three), I fell off a chair and broke my leg.

**b**  Algeria, the largest country in Africa, covers an area of nearly one million square miles.

**2 marks**

**3**  Rewrite the sentence below, using brackets or commas to punctuate the parenthesis.

When my grandparents first went to Spain long before it was a popular holiday destination they camped in a farmer's field.

_____

_____

**1 mark**

**4**  Rewrite the sentence below, adding the parenthesis 'even though we lost' in brackets.

The final was one of the most exciting and enjoyable matches that I have played in.

_____

_____

**1 mark**

**5**  Use the words below to write a sentence that includes a parenthesis in brackets.

my pen pal          Henri          lives in France

_____

_____

**1 mark**

**6**  Rewrite the sentence below using commas to punctuate the parenthesis.

I do my homework which we get almost every day as soon as I get home from school.

_____

_____

**1 mark**

10

**7** Use the words below to write a sentence that includes a parenthesis in brackets.

my aunt          my father's sister          lives in Scotland

**1** mark

_____

_____

**8** Rewrite the sentence below, adding the parenthesis that Roald Dahl is a popular children's author.

Roald Dahl wrote many of his books in his garden shed.

**1** mark

_____

_____

**9** In which section is the punctuation mistake? Circle the correct number.

**1** mark

When my brother wants to / annoy me which is / most of the time, he repeats / everything I say.

1                    2                    3                    4

**10** Rewrite the sentence below, punctuating the parenthesis using brackets.

On my birthday, Mum made me chocolate cake which is my favourite and a huge pizza smothered in cheese.

**1** mark

_____

_____

**11** Rewrite the sentence below, punctuating the parenthesis.

After breakfast but before I go to school I always do ten minutes' piano practice.

**1** mark

_____

_____

**12** Use the words below to write a sentence that includes a parenthesis.

my dog          ate my homework          a terrier called Brian

**1** mark

_____

_____

**Time to reflect**

**Mark your test out of 13. How did you do?**

Check your answers in the back of the book. If any of your answers are incorrect, go to practice section 1 in Practice Book 2 to revise this topic.

# 6 Prepositions

In this test you will practise identifying and using prepositions that give information about time, place, direction and cause.

⏱ **10**

**1**   Underline the preposition of place in the sentence below.

We parked the car outside the house.

**1 mark**

**2**   **a**   Which preposition completes the sentence below? Tick **one** box.

When the sun came out, we went for a walk _____ the woods.

☐ between          ☐ through

☐ under            ☐ above

**b**   Which type of preposition is it? Tick **one** box.

☐ time             ☐ place

☐ direction        ☐ cause

**2 marks**

**3**   Complete the sentence below using a preposition of place.

I tidy my room by pushing all the mess _____ the bed.

**1 mark**

**4**   Which preposition of direction completes the sentence below? Tick **one** box.

If you carry on walking _____ the town hall, you eventually arrive at some traffic lights.

☐ near             ☐ through

☐ past             ☐ up

**1 mark**

**5**   Choose the correct preposition to complete the well-known phrase below.

Beauty is _____ the eye of the beholder.

in        above        at        towards

**1 mark**

**6**   **a**   Underline the preposition in the sentence below.

I have not been to see my cousins for ages.

**b**   Which type of preposition is it? Tick **one** box.

☐ time             ☐ place

☐ direction        ☐ cause

**2 marks**

**7** **a** Which preposition completes the sentence below? Tick **one** box.

You should always wash your hands _____ eating.

☐ until      ☐ while      ☐ before      ☐ through

**b** Which type of preposition is it? Tick **one** box.

**2**
**marks**

☐ time      ☐ direction      ☐ place      ☐ cause

**8** Underline the preposition of cause in the sentence below.

**1**
**mark**

We got there more quickly by running.

**9** Write a sentence about how you travel to school, using a preposition of cause.

**1**
**mark**

_____

_____

**10** Choose the correct preposition to complete the well-known phrase below.

You cannot make a silk purse _____ of a sow's ear.

**1**
**mark**

because      out      in      above

**11** Underline the prepositional phrase of cause in the sentence below.

**1**
**mark**

My mum bought me some goggles for swimming.

**12** **a** Choose the correct preposition to complete the well-known phrase below.

Don't try to run _____ you can walk.

up      inside      before      during

**b** Which type of preposition is it? Tick **one** box.

**2**
**marks**

☐ time      ☐ place      ☐ direction      ☐ cause

**Time to reflect**

**Mark your test out of 16. How did you do?**

Check your answers in the back of the book. If any of your answers are incorrect, go to practice section 2 in Practice Book 2 to revise this topic.

# 7 Conjunctions

In this test you will practise identifying and using conjunctions.

**10**

**1**   Which sentence below contains a coordinating conjunction? Tick **one** box.

☐ We played brilliantly for ninety minutes but did not score a goal.

☐ We were happy because we had done our best.

**1 mark**

**2**   Which coordinating conjunction completes the sentence below? Tick **one** box.

We took the dogs up into the hills _____ walked for miles.

☐ so                        ☐ or

☐ and                       ☐ but

**1 mark**

**3**   **a**   Underline the conjunction in the sentence below.

We laughed until we could not laugh anymore.

**b**   Which type of conjunction is it? Tick **one** box.

☐ subordinating                  ☐ coordinating

**2 marks**

**4**   Is the statement below true or false? Tick **one** box.

The words 'although', 'if', 'before' and 'because' can all be used as subordinating conjunctions.

☐ true                      ☐ false

**1 mark**

**5**   Is the statement below true or false? Tick **one** box.

Subordinating conjunctions link two subordinate clauses in a sentence.

☐ true                      ☐ false

**1 mark**

**6**   **a**   Which conjunction completes the sentence below? Tick **one** box.

It is my favourite film of all time _____ it always makes me feel happy.

☐ until                     ☐ because

☐ or                        ☐ although

**b**   Which type of conjunction is it?

_____

**2 marks**

**7**   Complete the sentence below using a coordinating conjunction.

Einstein was a genius _____ he had a very poor memory and was very forgetful.

**1 mark**

**8**   Which sentence below contains a coordinating conjunction? Tick **one** box.

☐ Cheetahs can run very fast but they tire very quickly.

☐ Because dolphins are mammals, they cannot breathe underwater.

**1 mark**

**9** Complete the sentence below using the correct conjunction.

*but   although   where   because*

I am sure I will get better _____ I practise every day.

**1 mark**

**10 a** Which conjunction completes the sentence below? Tick **one** box.

Henry VIII established the Church of England _____ is well-known for having had six wives.

☐ but

☐ because

☐ and

☐ since

**b** Which type of conjunction is it?

_____

**2 marks**

**11** Which of the sentences below contains a subordinating conjunction? Tick **one** box.

☐ Measure the butter and sugar, and place them in a bowl.

☐ Beat the butter and sugar until you have a smooth paste.

**1 mark**

**12** Complete the sentence below using the correct conjunction.

*and   if   but   before*

I can get up early in the morning _____ I go to bed at a sensible time.

**1 mark**

**13** Complete the sentence below using a coordinating conjunction.

The meal looked delicious _____

_____

**1 mark**

**14** Complete the sentence below using a subordinating conjunction.

I did all the washing up _____

_____

**1 mark**

### Time to reflect

**Mark your test out of 17. How did you do?**

Check your answers in the back of the book. If any of your answers are incorrect, go to practice section 3 in Practice Book 2 to revise this topic.

# 8 Direct speech

In this test you will practise punctuating direct speech accurately.

**(10)**

**1** Is the statement below true or false? Tick **one** box.

Direct speech should always have 'he said' or 'she said' after the spoken words.

☐ true          ☐ false

**1 mark**

**2** Which sentence below is punctuated correctly? Tick **one** box.

☐ 'I'm making spaghetti tomorrow,' said Dimitri.      ☐ 'I'm making spaghetti tomorrow' said Dimitri.

☐ 'I'm making spaghetti tomorrow, said Dimitri.      ☐ 'I'm making spaghetti tomorrow, said Dimitri.'

**1 mark**

**3** In which section is the punctuation mistake? Circle the correct number.

'Turn the game off now,' / said Dad, / 'or I'm going to hide that / machine for a month'

       1            2            3            4

**1 mark**

**4** Rewrite the sentence below using the correct punctuation.

you must put your hand up and wait patiently said Ms Choudhuri if you want to answer a question

_____

_____

**1 mark**

**5** The text below has the correct punctuation but incorrect layout. Mark the places where a new paragraph should begin using a double slash (//).

'How many have you got?' asked Jamie. 'I've got three,' said Aled. 'And I've got four,' laughed Adi, 'so I win.'

**1 mark**

**6** Underline all the words in the text below that should begin with a capital letter.

'there is only one rule in this club,' said the coach, 'and it's that you should try your hardest and do your best at all times.'

'what if my best is not very good?' asked Marta.

**1 mark**

**7** In which section is the punctuation mistake? Circle the correct number.

'That will be three pounds exactly,' / said the shopkeeper. / Unless I can interest you / in a very special offer.'

       1            2            3            4

**1 mark**

**8** Which sentence below is punctuated correctly? Tick **one** box.

☐ 'I looked on the internet' said Zak 'and found all the information that I needed.'      ☐ 'I looked on the internet,' said Zak, 'and found all the information that I needed.'

☐ 'I looked on the internet,' said Zak and found all the information that I needed.'      ☐ 'I looked on the internet,' said Zak, 'And found all the information that I needed.'

**1 mark**

**9**   Rewrite the sentence below using the correct punctuation.

Neil Armstrong said that's one small step for man, one giant leap for mankind when he took his first step on the surface of the moon

_____

_____

**1 mark**

**10**   In which section is the punctuation mistake? Circle the correct number.

'If the laptop freezes' / said my brother, 'you need to / turn it off and / on again.'

        1              2              3              4

**1 mark**

**11**   The text below has the correct punctuation but incorrect layout. Mark the places where a new paragraph should begin using a double slash (//).

'What did you get on the test?' Charlie asked. 'I got full marks,' he added, smiling. 'I got two wrong,' said Ben, 'but it wasn't fair because I was late.' 'Being on time is all part of the test,' laughed Charlie.

**1 mark**

**12**   Underline all the words in the text below that should begin with a capital letter.

"mum, can I have a pony?" asked Amy.

"a pony?" shrieked Mum, "where would we keep it?"

"it could live in my room," said Amy.

"how would it get up the stairs?" asked Mum.

**1 mark**

**13**   Rewrite the sentence below using the correct punctuation.

I have never she sighed in my life she added been so disappointed

_____

**1 mark**

**14**   Which sentence below is punctuated incorrectly? Tick **one** box.

☐ 'We're not going on holiday,' said Dad, 'because we're saving up for a special holiday next year.'

☐ 'Where are we going next year?' gasped my little sister excitedly.

☐ 'That would be telling,' said Dad, tapping his nose mysteriously.

☐ 'I bet it's somewhere really boring,' moaned my brother, 'It usually is.'

**1 mark**

## Time to reflect

### Mark your test out of 14. How did you do?

Check your answers in the back of the book. If any of your answers are incorrect, go to practice section 4 in Practice Book 2 to revise this topic.

# 9 Colons, semi-colons and dashes

In this test you will practise using colons, semi-colons and dashes accurately.

**10**

1 Is the statement below true or false? Tick **one** box.

You should always use a colon to introduce a list.

☐ true                    ☐ false

**1 mark**

2 Which sentence below uses a colon incorrectly? Tick **one** box.

☐ There are three key ways to be environmentally friendly: reduce the waste you create, reuse things instead of throwing them away, and recycle anything that cannot be reused.

☐ The witches predict Macbeth's future: 'All hail, Macbeth, that shalt be king hereafter!'

☐ To make pancakes: you will need just three ingredients eggs, milk and flour.

☐ There is only one way to get fit: exercise more!

**1 mark**

3 Punctuate the sentence below using a semi-colon.

Many people believe dinosaurs were wiped out by a massive meteorite others argue that it was due to a sharp increase in volcanic activity.

**1 mark**

4 Punctuate the sentence below using a colon.

I need to do this homework quickly it is due in tomorrow.

**1 mark**

5 Rewrite the sentence below using semi-colons to punctuate the list.

To build a hedgehog restaurant, you will need: a wooden or plastic box, one with a lid is ideal, a sharp knife (and an adult to help you use it), some strong sticky tape, e.g. duct tape, and some old bricks or large stones.

_____

_____

_____

_____

**1 mark**

6 Rewrite the sentence below using a dash.

That film made me cry I had to turn it off.

_____

**1 mark**

7 Which sentence below uses a semi-colon incorrectly? Tick **one** box.

☐ I went skating; I was terrified.

☐ I fell over; I got back up.

☐ I kept trying; eventually I got better.

☐ I went home; feeling exhausted.

**1 mark**

**8** Rewrite the sentence below using a colon.

Computer games are addictive you can spend hours playing and still want to play more.

**1 mark**

_____

**9** Rewrite the sentence below using a semi-colon.

Computer games are addictive they are designed to be.

**1 mark**

_____

**10** Rewrite the sentence below using colons and semi-colons.

Lots of relatives came camping with us, my uncle, who loves camping, my aunt, who hates camping, and my three cousins, who are very small and annoying.

_____

_____

**1 mark**

_____

**11** Which sentence below is punctuated incorrectly? Tick **one** box.

☐ I got back on the bike – there was no way I was giving up!

☐ The sun was shining: the breeze was warm.

☐ I walked for miles through the snow; I was frozen.

**1 mark**

☐ Before you start writing, make sure you do one thing: make a plan.

**12** Rewrite the sentence below using correct punctuation.

There are several species that are unique to Australia, calm, gentle koalas that can sleep for 20 hours a day, energetic kangaroos that can cover 7 metres in one hop, and many, many others.

_____

_____

_____

**1 mark**

_____

### Time to reflect

### Mark your test out of 12. How did you do?

Check your answers in the back of the book. If any of your answers are incorrect, go to practice section 5 in Practice Book 2 to revise this topic.

# 10 Apostrophes

In this test you will practise using apostrophes accurately in contractions and to show possession.

**(10)**

**1**  Rewrite the sentence below using a contraction.

I have not got any time to lose.

_____

**1**
mark

**2**  Rewrite the sentence below using two contractions.

I would if I could but I cannot so I will not.

_____

**1**
mark

**3**  Which sentence below is punctuated correctly? Tick **one** box.

☐ Dad put Lucas socks in the wash.

☐ Dad put Lucas's socks in the wash.

☐ Dad put Lucases socks in the wash.

☐ Dad put Lucas's sock's in the wash.

**1**
mark

**4**  Punctuate the sentence below using a possessive apostrophe.

The Romans engineering techniques were highly advanced, enabling them to build roads, tunnels, bridges and aqueducts.

**1**
mark

**5**  Circle the correct spellings in brackets in the sentence below.

The mole has very poor eyesight but finds (its' / it's / its) way using the sense of touch and (its' / it's / its) hair and whiskers to detect vibrations in the soil.

**2**
marks

**6**  Rewrite the sentence below using a possessive apostrophe.

The hamster belonging to Lois loves carrots.

_____

**1**
mark

**7**  In which section is the punctuation mistake? Circle the correct number.

All the dog's tails / started wagging when / Billy's mum opened / the packet of dog treats.

       1                 2              3              4

**1**
mark

**8**  Circle the correct spelling in brackets in the sentence below.

I spent a long time writing this story and I think (its' / it's / its) really good.

**1**
mark

**9**  Rewrite the sentence below using a possessive apostrophe.

Elena has borrowed the calculator belonging to her friend.

_____

**1**
mark

**10** Which sentence below is punctuated correctly? Tick **one** box.

☐ My mums' gone to my sister's school to watch a play.

☐ My mum's gone to my sisters school to watch a play.

☐ My mum's gone to my sister's school to watch a play.

☐ My mums gone to my sister's school to watch a play.

**1 mark**

**11** In which section is the punctuation mistake? Circle the correct number.

It's hard to believe / that a chameleon's tongue can / be one and a half times the / length of it's body.

        1                2                3                4

**1 mark**

**12** Circle the correct spelling in brackets in the sentence below.

The cinema opens (its' / it's / its) doors to the public at 2 pm.

**1 mark**

**13** Punctuate the sentence below using a possessive apostrophe.

My grandmas cat is very moody.

**1 mark**

**14** Rewrite the sentence below using two contractions.

He should not ask if he does not want to hear the answer.

_____

_____

**1 mark**

**15** Which sentence below is punctuated correctly? Tick **one** box.

☐ Its Tom's birthday so we're having a party.

☐ It's Toms' birthday so we're having a party.

☐ It's Tom's birthday so wer'e having a party.

☐ It's Tom's birthday so we're having a party.

**1 mark**

**16** In which section is the punctuation mistake? Circle the correct number.

I'm sorry that I / dropped my brother's phone / and broke its screen / but it really was'nt my fault.

        1                2                3                4

**1 mark**

## Time to reflect

### Mark your test out of 17. How did you do?

Check your answers in the back of the book. If any of your answers are incorrect, go to practice section 6 in Practice Book 2 to revise this topic.

# 11 Prefixes and suffixes

In this test you will practise spelling using of a range of prefixes and suffixes.

**1** Underline the stressed syllable in each word below.

referred          reference          occurrence          difference

**1** mark

**2** Underline the correctly spelled word in brackets to complete each sentence below.

**a** The film was so (hilarious / hilareous), I was still laughing as we left the cinema.

**b** After the cinema, we went for a (delicious / deliceous) meal.

**c** The burger was lovely but not very (nutriteous / nutritious).

**3** marks

**3** Add the prefix **mis-** or **dis-** to each of the words below to give it the **opposite** meaning.

_____appear          _____connect          _____behave          _____honest

**1** mark

**4** Circle the correctly spelled word in brackets to complete the sentences below.

Our homework was to (write / wright) a (frightening / fritening) story. We were given just one (night / nite) to complete it. I thought it was going to take until (midnite / midnight) and I was (rite / right).

**1** mark

**5** Rewrite the root words below, adding the suffix **–ing**.

love                    write                    believe                    dance

_____     _____     _____     _____

**1** mark

**6** Complete the sentences below by adding a suffix to each of the words in brackets to form an adjective.

**a** The explorers were _____ . (adventure)

**b** The journey was very _____ . (hazard)

**c** Luckily, they were highly _____ . (courage)

**d** When they made it home, they became extremely _____ . (fame)

**4** marks

**7** Complete the sentences below by adding the suffix -**able** or -**ible** to the unfinished words.

My brother loves his new coat. He thinks it is comfort_____ and fashion_____ . He also thinks

it makes him invis_____ . I know it seems imposs_____ and unbeliev_____ but it's true.

He isn't very sens_____ .

**6** marks

**8** Add the prefix **im-** or **ir-** to each of the words below to give it the **opposite** meaning.

_____relevant          _____patient          _____mobile          _____resistible

**4** marks

**9** Complete the sentences below by adding a suffix to each of the root words in brackets.

**a** The internet is a wonderful source of _____ . (inform)

**b** The secret of doing a job well is _____ . (prepare)

**c** The charity says it is looking forward to receiving my _____ . (donate)

**d** She answered the teacher's question without _____ . (hesitate)

**4 marks**

**10** Add the prefix **in-** or **il-** to each of the words below to give it the **opposite** meaning.

_____correct         _____logical         _____literate         _____destructible

**4 marks**

**11** Circle the correct spelling in each pair below.

**a** different / differant         **b** brillient / brilliant         **c** assistent / assistant

**d** intelligent / intelligant         **e** pleasent / pleasant

**5 marks**

**12** Complete the words in the sentences below by adding the suffix **-cial** or **-tial**.

**a** Revision is essen_____ .

**b** You need to make a spe_____ effort.

**c** Her ini_____ reaction was surprise.

**d** My mum bought me an offi_____ England rugby shirt.

**4 marks**

**13** Complete the sentences below by adding a suffix to each of the root words in brackets.

**a** When United won the cup, we had a huge _____ . (celebrate)

**b** The theme park rides are a great _____ . (attract)

**c** Throwing a party takes a lot of _____ . (organise)

**d** For homework I had to write a _____ of my favourite meal. (describe)

**4 marks**

**14** Add the prefix **mis-**, **dis-**, **in-**, **im-**, **ir-** or **il-** to each of the words below to give it the **opposite** meaning.

_____perfect         _____dependent         _____spell

_____interested         _____regular

**5 marks**

## Time to reflect

### Mark your test out of 47. How did you do?

Check your answers in the back of the book. If any of your answers are incorrect, go to practice section 5 in Practice Book 1 to revise this topic.

# 12 Plural nouns and tricky spellings

In this test you will practise forming plural nouns and spelling words that do not follow the usual rules.

**1** Which spelling below is correct? Tick **one** box.

⬜ embarisd      ⬜ embarassed

⬜ embarrassed      ⬜ embarrased

**1** mark

**2** Find the spelling mistake in each of the sentences below and then write the correct spelling.

**a** We sliced each loaf of bread into two halfs.

_____

**b** Two elderly ladys knocked on our door this morning.

_____

**c** I helped push the trolley but I could not reach the top shelfs in the supermarket.

_____

**d** I have been invited to two different partys this week.

_____

**4** marks

**3** Complete the sentences below using the correct spellings of the words in brackets.

**a** We carried out a _____ search for my pencil case. (through / thurough / thorough)

**b** My _____ is better but I still have a sore throat. (coff / cough / coph)

**c** The sea was so _____ that we could not go swimming. (ruff / rouff / rough)

**3** marks

**4** Write the correct plural of each of the words below.

**a** bucket _____    **b** brush _____    **c** family _____

**3** marks

**5** Complete the sentences below, using the plural form of the word in brackets.

**a** There were about a hundred _____ in the road. (sheep)

**b** I ran outside so fast that I had no time to put any shoes on my _____ . (foot)

**c** It was so heavy, it took three _____ to lift it. (person)

**3** marks

**6** In which section is the mistake? Circle the correct number.

If I had three wishs, / I would wish for two ponies, / two puppies / and two goldfish.

     1           2           3           4

**1** mark

**7** Circle the correctly spelled plural below.

quizs          quizzes          quizzs

**1** mark

**8** Write the correct plural of each of the words below.

**3** marks

**a** gentleman _____    **b** baby _____    **c** child _____

**9** Which spelling below is correct? Tick **one** box.

**1** mark

☐ definitely                    ☐ deffinatley

☐ definately                    ☐ deffiniteley

**10** Complete the sentences below using the correct spellings of the words in brackets.

**a** The wicked _____ hated Snow White. (qeuen / queen / qeeun)

**b** We had to wait hours in a _____ for the bus. (queue / qeue / que)

**3** marks

**c** We couldn't see through the glass because it was _____ . (opake / opaque / opaqeu)

**11** Circle the correct plural spelling in each pair below.

**a** witches / witchs            **b** princesses / princessies

**4** marks

**c** kissies / kisses            **d** splashs / splashes

**12** In which section is the mistake? Circle the correct number.

**1** mark

When I was young, / Grandad told us / all kinds of storys / about the countries he had visited.

1                    2                    3                    4

**13** Complete the sentences below, using the correct spellings of the words in brackets.

**a** My brother and I _____ a lot. (argyou / argeu / argue)

**b** I have a very _____ memory of my first day at school. (vague / vageu / vage)

**3** marks

**c** In the 1660s, thousands of people died of the _____ . (plageu / plague / plage)

**14** Find the spelling mistake in each of the sentences below and then write the correct spelling.

**a** My pencil case contains everything that is necesary for the test.

_____

**b** They hid themselfs in the bushes so well that no one could find them.

**2** marks

_____

### Time to reflect

**Mark your test out of 33. How did you do?**

Check your answers in the back of the book. If any of your answers are incorrect, go to practice section 6 in Practice Book 1 to revise this topic.

# 13 Silent letters

In this test you will practise spelling words that contain silent letters.

**1** Which spelling below is correct? Tick **one** box.

☐ orchestra ☐ orcestra ☐ orchesstra

`1 mark`

**2** Complete the sentences below using words that contain a silent **h**.

**a** _____ did you do when you fell over?

**b** _____ did you fall over?

**c** _____ did you fall over?

`3 marks`

**3** Complete the sentence below by filling in the missing silent letters.

I ___rote down an ans___er but I think I got it ___rong.

`3 marks`

**4** In which section is the mistake? Circle the correct number.

I went home, / went up to my room, / coamed my hair / and changed my clothes.
      1             2             3             4

`3 marks`

**5** Complete the sentence below by filling in the missing silent letters.

My favourite subjects at sc___ool are c___emistry and tec___nology.

`1 mark`

**6** Complete the sentences below by circling the correct spellings in brackets.

**a** The film lasted for two and a half (hours / ours).

**b** Poems do not have to (rhyme / rymb).

**c** She is my favourite (carachter / character) in the story.

`3 marks`

**7** Complete the sentences below by circling the correct spellings in brackets.

**a** When I grow up, I want to be a professional (wrestler / wresler / restler).

**b** I injured my (nee / knee / knea) while playing football.

**c** It feels like I have pulled a (musel / muscle / muscel).

`3 marks`

**8** Which spelling below is correct? Tick **one** box.

☐ knolege ☐ knowlege ☐ knowledge

`1 mark`

**9** Complete the sentence below by filling in the missing silent letters.

The ___night took out his s___ord and ___nocked on the door of the cas___le.

`4 marks`

**10** In which section is the mistake? Circle the correct number.

My dog ate / a whole birthday cake and then howled / all night because he / had a stomac ache.

          1                          2                            3                        4

**11** Complete the sentences below using words that contain a silent **b**.

**a** I ate a crumbly biscuit and left a pile of _____ all over the floor.

**b** I was certain that I would go to bed early tonight, but now I am beginning to _____ it.

**c** We slowly _____ up the hill and then scrambled back down again.

**12** Which spelling below is correct? Tick **one** box.

☐ fasinating                    ☐ fashinating                  ☐ fascinating

**13** In which section is the mistake? Circle the correct number.

In the first seen / of the play, three witches / are seen on the stage, / which is a frightening sight.

          1                          2                            3                        4

**14** Complete the sentences below by circling the correct spellings in brackets.

**a** I like to (wrap / rap) presents in colourful paper.

**b** I read the (hole / whole) book in just three hours.

**c** I have never been to a (foreign / forein) country.

**15** Complete the sentences below using words that contain a silent letter.

**a** You should always be careful when using _____ because it is very easy to cut yourself.

**b** I sprained my _____ when I was playing netball.

**c** If you shout 'hello' in a cave you will hear an _____ of your voice shouting 'hello' back.

**16** Complete the sentences below by filling in the missing silent letters.

I heard a strange scra___ching sound coming from the cu___board. I looked inside and spent a minute or

t___o waiting, wa___ching and lis___ening to see if I cou___d see w___at it was. I ___new there was

something in there.

**Time to reflect**

### Mark your test out of 42. How did you do?

Check your answers in the back of the book. If any of your answers are incorrect, go to practice section 7 in Practice Book 1 to revise this topic.

# 14 Homophones and homonyms

In this test you will practise using homophones and homonyms accurately.

**⏱ 10**

**1**  Is the statement below true or false? Tick **one** box.

'Main' and 'mane' are examples of homonyms.

☐ true                    ☐ false

**1 mark**

**2**  Complete the sentences below using these homophones.

aloud            allowed

**a**  I always feel nervous when my teacher asks me to read _____ .

**b**  You are not _____ to move once you have chosen your hiding place.

**2 marks**

**3**  Underline the correct homophone in brackets in each of the sentences below.

**a**  They brought (they're / there / their) own sandwiches for lunch.

**b**  Inside the box, (they're / there / their) were two sandwiches, an apple and a yoghurt.

**c**  Cheese sandwiches are nice but (they're / there / their) not my favourite.

**3 marks**

**4**  The word 'spring' is a homonym. It can mean 'to jump up'. Write a definition of another of its meanings.

_____

**1 mark**

**5**  Write two sentences including the homophones below.

whether            weather

1  _____

2  _____

**2 marks**

**6**  The sentence below uses the homonym 'fair'. Write a sentence using an alternative meaning of 'fair'.

Aunt Matilda has blue eyes and long, fair hair.

_____

**1 mark**

**7**  Complete the sentences below with the correct homophones.

whose            who's

**a**  I wonder _____ going to win.

**b**  The winner is the player _____ score is the lowest.

**2 marks**

**8**  The word 'can' is a homonym. It can mean 'to be able to'. Write a definition of another of its meanings.

_____

**1 mark**

**9** Underline the correct homophone in brackets in each of the sentences below.

**3 marks**

    **a** I have no idea (where / were / wear) I am going.

    **b** I have no idea what I am going to (where / were / wear) for the party.

    **c** I have no idea if they (where / were / wear) right or wrong.

**10** Write two separate sentences, each using the homonym 'lie' in a different way.

**2 marks**

    1 _____

    2 _____

**11** Complete the sentences below with the correct homophones.

    passed          past

**2 marks**

    **a** I have to go to the dentist at half _____ three.

    **b** I _____ the sweet shop on the way to the dentist's surgery.

**12** Write two sentences including the homophones below.

    peace          piece

**2 marks**

    1 _____

    2 _____

**13** The sentence below uses the homonym 'wave'. Write a sentence using an alternative meaning of 'wave'.

    A huge wave crashed onto the beach, soaking us with spray.

**1 mark**

_____

**14** Underline the correct homophone in brackets in each of the sentences below.

    **a** If you do not know what to do, your teacher will (advice / advise) you.

**3 marks**

    **b** If you watch live television, you must have a television (licence / license).

    **c** If you (practice / practise), you will find it gets much easier.

### Time to reflect

**Mark your test out of 26. How did you do?**

Check your answers in the back of the book. If any of your answers are incorrect, go to practice section 7 in Practice Book 2 to revise this topic.

# 15 ie/ei and ough spellings

In this test you will practise spelling words that contain the letter strings **ie**, **ei** and **ough**.

⏱ **10**

**1** Circle the correct spelling in each pair below.

    **a**    deceitful / decietful              **b**    mischievous / mischeivous

                                                                       **2** marks

**2** Read the definition below and complete the word using **ie** or **ei**.

     A piece of paper that shows that an item has been paid for: rec _____ pt

                                                                       **1** mark

**3** Which word below rhymes with 'cow'? Tick **one** box.

     ☐ rough                    ☐ thorough                 ☐ plough

                                                                       **1** mark

**4** Write an **ough** word that means 'a small fried cake of sweet dough, sometimes filled with jam or custard'.

     _____

                                                                       **1** mark

**5** In which section is the mistake? Circle the correct number.

     My sister would not stop / shouting when I was / trying to revise; she / can be so thougtless.

                 1                         2                       3                      4              **1** mark

**6** Circle the correct spelling in each pair below.

    **a**    sheild / shield                     **b**    chief / cheif

                                                                            **2** marks

**7** Complete the sentence below using **ie** or **ei**.

     He was so tall, his hair was nearly touching the c _____ ling.

                                                                       **1** mark

**8** Which word below rhymes with 'go'? Tick **one** box.

     ☐ through                  ☐ though                  ☐ bough

                                                                       **1** mark

**9** Write the plural of the word below.

     party _____

                                                                        **1** mark

**10** In which section is the mistake? Circle the correct number.

     I thought I / had brort my football / boots but I must have left / them at home.

            1                  2                       3                    4              **1** mark

**11** Complete the sentence below using an **ei** or **ie** word.

     Some people think they exist, but I do not _____ in ghosts.

                                                                       **1** mark

**12** Write an **ough** word that means 'as much as you need'.

     _____

                                                                       **1** mark

**13** In which section is the spelling mistake? Circle the correct number.

*1 mark*

I was disappointed with / my score / but Mum thought / that I'd acheived a lot.

       1             2          3         4

**14** Complete the sentence below using an **ei** or **ie** word.

*1 mark*

It was a huge _____ when I got to the end of the performance without making a mistake.

**15** Write the plural of the word below.

*1 mark*

galaxy _____

**16** Circle the correct spelling in each pair below.

*2 marks*

**a**   brief / breif                           **b**   receive / recieve

**17** Write an **ough** word that means 'a container that farm animals eat or drink from'.

*1 mark*

t _____

**18** Read the definition below and complete the word using **ie** or **ei**.

*1 mark*

A loud, high-pitched sound, often suggesting shock or fear: shr _____ k

**19** Write a sentence about a car journey using an **ough** word.

*1 mark*

_____

_____

**20** Complete the sentence below using an **ei** or **ie** word and an **ough** word.

*2 marks*

Of all the different _____ my uncle has visited, he says Australia is the one that I

_____ to visit when I am older.

**21** In which section is the mistake? Circle the correct number.

*1 mark*

Running up the hills / was tough / althogh not as tiring as / running through the muddy fields.

       1             2          3         4

### Time to reflect

**Mark your test out of 25. How did you do?**

Check your answers in the back of the book. If any of your answers are incorrect, go to practice section 8 in Practice Book 2 to revise this topic.

# 16 Tricky spellings

In this test you will practise spelling tricky words, including ones with double letters and unstressed sounds.

**10**

**1** Read the definition below and complete the word.

A book containing the meanings of thousands of words: d _____

1 mark

**2** Complete the sentence below by adding a suffix to the root word 'shop'.

This afternoon we are going to go _____ .

1 mark

**3** Which word below is spelled correctly? Tick **one** box.

☐ tomorrow          ☐ tomorow          ☐ tommorrow

1 mark

**4** What are the words below all examples of?

digestive     shortbread     ginger nut     custard cream

_____

1 mark

**5** Complete the word below.

diff ___ rent

1 mark

**6** Which sentence below is spelled correctly? Tick **one** box.

☐ Bookking tickets for the cinema is not always neccessary.

☐ Booking tickets for the cinema is not always necessary.

☐ Booking tickets for the cinema is not always necesary.

☐ Bookking tickets for the cinema is not always necessary.

1 mark

**7** Which word below is spelled correctly? Tick **one** box.

☐ remembar     ☐ remember     ☐ rememba     ☐ remmember

1 mark

**8** In which section is the mistake? Circle the correct number.

When I am older / I plan to / start my own buisness / selling sandwiches.
　　　　　1　　　　　　2　　　　　　3　　　　　　　　4

1 mark

**9** Complete the word below.

sep ___ rate

1 mark

**10** Complete the sentence below by adding a suffix to the root word 'add'.

You can get the total by _____ the two numbers together.

1 mark

**11** Read the definitions below and complete the words.

**a** A plant eaten as food, for example: cabbage, peas or sprouts: v _____

**b** People you are related to, for example: parents, cousins and siblings: f _____

2 marks

**12** Complete the sentence below using the present progressive tense of the verbs 'hop', 'skip', 'run' and 'jump'.

**4 marks**

My little brother went _____ , _____ , _____ and

_____ all the way to the playground.

**13** Add a suffix to the adjective below to form an adverb that means 'very'.

**1 mark**

real _____

**14** Which word below is spelled correctly? Tick **one** box.

**1 mark**

☐ choclate          ☐ chocolate          ☐ chocalate          ☐ chockerlat

**15** What are the descriptions below all examples of?

| 10 Lark Street | 17 Oakley Gardens | 4 Acacia Drive |
| Thornbridge | Upton | Edgemond |
| TH29 0BP | GN14 8DW | EG7 9QZ |

**1 mark**

_____

**16** Complete the word below.

**1 mark**

mis ___ rable

**17** Complete the past tense verbs in the sentences below.

**2 marks**

**a**  Mum grin _____ from ear to ear when I told her I had tidied my room.

**b**  Dad drop _____ me off at the leisure centre for my judo class.

**18** Which sentence below is spelled incorrectly? Tick **one** box.

**1 mark**

☐ I was putting on my school uniform.          ☐ My sister started chating to me.

☐ She said we might be getting a puppy.          ☐ I said I thought she was fibbing.

**19** In which section is the mistake? Circle the correct number.

**1 mark**

I was sitting in front of / the television but I turned it / off because there was / nothing intresting to watch.

1                    2                    3                    4

### Time to reflect

**Mark your test out of 24. How did you do?**

Check your answers in the back of the book. If any of your answers are incorrect, go to practice section 9 in Practice Book 2 to revise this topic.

# 17 Locating information

In this test you will practise finding information in an extract from a novel.

*This extract is from 'Treasure Island' by Robert Louis Stevenson. The narrator lives and works in his father's inn.*

**10**

About three o'clock of a bitter, foggy, frosty afternoon, I was standing at the door for a moment, when I saw someone drawing slowly near along the road. He was plainly blind, for he tapped before him with a stick and wore a great green shade over his eyes and nose; and he was hunched, as if with age or weakness. I never saw in my life a more dreadful-looking figure. He stopped a little from the inn, and raising his voice in an odd sing-song, addressed the air in front of him,

'Will any kind friend inform a poor blind man, who has lost the precious sight of his eyes, where or in what part of this country he may now be?'

'You are at the Admiral Benbow, Black Hill Cove, my good man,' said I.

'I hear a voice," said he, 'a young voice. Will you give me your hand, my kind young friend, and lead me in?'

I held out my hand, and the horrible, soft-spoken, eyeless creature gripped it in a moment like a vice. I was so much startled that I struggled to withdraw, but the blind man pulled me close up to him with a single action of his arm.

'Now, boy,' he said, 'take me in to the captain.'

'Sir,' said I, 'I dare not.'

'Oh,' he sneered, 'Take me in straight or I'll break your arm.'

And he gave it, as he spoke, a wrench that made me cry out.

**abc** 'The Admiral Benbow' is the name of the inn.

**1** Where was the narrator standing when he first saw the blind man? Write your answer below.

_____

**1** mark

**2 a** In which season do you think this part of the story takes place? Tick **one** box.

☐ summer          ☐ winter

**b** Which words tell you this? Find and copy them.

_____

**2** marks

**3** Find and copy the word that means the same as:

**a** not standing up straight. _____          **b** surprised. _____

**2** marks

**4** The narrator says 'I saw someone drawing slowly near along the road'. What does 'drawing slowly near' mean here? Tick **one** box.

☐ slowly walking away from the narrator

☐ slowly approaching the narrator

☐ slowly taking something out of his pocket

**1** mark

**5** The narrator says 'He was plainly blind'. What does 'plainly' mean here? Tick **one** box.

☐ obviously or clearly

☐ in a boring or uninteresting way

☐ in a simple and basic way

**1** mark

**6** **a** Is the statement below true or false? Tick **one** box.

The narrator is frightened or anxious when he first sees the blind man.

☐ true                    ☐ false

**b** Which words tell you this? Find and copy them.

**2 marks**

_____

**7** Find and copy the word that means the same as 'valuable' or 'treasured'.

**1 mark**

_____

**8** **a** What age is the narrator? Tick **one** box.

☐ He is a baby.          ☐ He is a teenager.          ☐ He is an adult.

**b** Which words tell you this? Find and copy them.

**2 marks**

_____

_____

**9** **a** What is the blind man's manner at the beginning of the extract? Tick **one** box.

☐ angry and violent          ☐ polite and friendly

**b** Which words tell you this? Find and copy them.

**2 marks**

_____

**10** The narrator says 'I held out my hand, and the horrible, soft-spoken, eyeless creature gripped it in a moment like a vice.' What does the phrase 'like a vice' mean here? Tick **one** box.

**1 mark**

☐ carefully and precisely          ☐ angrily          ☐ firmly and powerfully

**11** Why does the blind man hurt the narrator? Tick **one** box.

**1 mark**

☐ because the narrator will not tell him where they are     ☐ because the narrator will not take him to see the captain     ☐ because the narrator thinks the blind man is frightening

**12** The narrator says the blind man gave his arm 'a wrench that made me cry out'. What does the word 'wrench' mean here? Tick **one** box.

**1 mark**

☐ a sudden violent pull          ☐ a large, heavy spanner          ☐ an angry look

## Time to reflect

### Mark your test out of 17. How did you do?

Check your answers in the back of the book. If any of your answers are incorrect, go to practice section 8 in Practice Book 1 to revise this topic.

# 18 Language for effect

In this test you will practise identifying and explaining literary techniques such as metaphors, similes, alliteration and onomatopoeia, which are used to create interesting and descriptive effects.

*This extract is from 'The Lady of Shalott' by Alfred, Lord Tennyson. It is about a beautiful lady who lives in a castle.*

**10**

## The Lady of Shalott

Willows whiten, aspens shiver.
The sunbeam showers break and quiver
In the stream that runneth ever
By the island in the river
Flowing down to Camelot.
Four gray walls, and four gray towers
Overlook a space of flowers,
And the silent isle imbowers
The Lady of Shalott.

Underneath the bearded barley,
The reaper, reaping late and early,
Hears her ever chanting cheerly,
Like an angel, singing clearly,
O'er the stream of Camelot.
Piling the sheaves in furrows airy,
Beneath the moon, the reaper weary
Listening whispers, 'Tis the fairy,
Lady of Shalott.'

**abc**
- An 'aspen' is a type of tree.
- 'Camelot' is the name of a castle.
- 'Imbowers' is an old-fashioned word meaning 'to surround or shelter'.

**1 a** Find and copy one metaphor about the sun in the first verse.

_____

**b** Explain in your own words what this suggests about the sun.

_____

_____

**2**
marks

**2 a** Find and copy one simile about the Lady of Shalott in the second verse.

_____

**b** Explain in your own words what this suggests about the Lady of Shallot.

_____

_____

**2**
marks

**3** Which literary technique is used in the words 'bearded barley'? Write your answer below.

_____

**1**
mark

*This extract is from a short story called 'The Treasure Chest' by David Grant. In this section, a boy named Jam is exploring the attic in his new house.*

Over in the corner of the attic, across the dusty floorboards, beyond the forest of old carpets rolled and propped up against the walls, past the spiders' webs shredded and shivering in the cold air, Jam could see a small wooden box. It was battered and dented and bound with a band of rusting iron like a pirate's treasure chest.

Before he knew what he was doing, he had pulled himself up through the attic hatch and, step by step, breath by breath, was making his way across the creaking, groaning floorboards towards the box.

When he reached it, he stopped. He stood, as cold and still as a stone, staring at the words scratched into the lid. DO NOT OPEN, they said. He read the words aloud – but still he knelt down and, with trembling hands, loosened the clasp on the rusting iron band, pulled up the lid of the box and peered into its darkness.

**4** Which literary technique is used in the words below? Tick **one** box.

beyond the forest of old carpets rolled and propped up against the walls

| | |
|---|---|
| ☐ metaphor | ☐ simile |
| ☐ onomatopoeia | ☐ alliteration |

**1 mark**

**5** Which two literary techniques are used in the words below? Tick **one** box.

spiders' webs shredded and shivering in the cold air

| | |
|---|---|
| ☐ metaphor and alliteration | ☐ alliteration and personification |
| ☐ personification and onomatopoeia | ☐ onomatopoeia and metaphor |

**1 mark**

**6** Which literary technique is used in the words below? Tick **one** box.

groaning floorboards

| | |
|---|---|
| ☐ metaphor | ☐ alliteration |
| ☐ personication | ☐ simile |

**1 mark**

**7** Find and copy one example of onomatopoeia in the text.

_____

**1 mark**

**8** Find and copy one example of a simile in the text.

_____

**1 mark**

### Time to reflect

**Mark your test out of 10. How did you do?**

Check your answers in the back of the book. If any of your answers are incorrect, go to practice section 9 in Practice Book 1 to revise this topic.

# 19 Inference

In this test you will practise using your skills of inference to work out information from a text.

*This extract is from 'Pollyanna' by Eleanor H. Porter. It is about a girl who lives with her aunt.*

**10**

The little room was cooler now, and the air blew in fresh and sweet. Outside, the birds were twittering joyously, and Pollyanna flew to the window to talk to them. She saw then that down in the garden her aunt was already out among the rosebushes. With rapid fingers, therefore, she made herself ready to join her.

Down the attic stairs sped Pollyanna, leaving both doors wide open. Through the hall, down the next flight, then bang through the front screened-door and around to the garden, she ran.

Aunt Polly was leaning over a rose-bush when Pollyanna, gurgling with delight, flung herself upon her.

'Oh, Aunt Polly, Aunt Polly, I reckon I am glad this morning just to be alive!'

'PollyANNA!' remonstrated the lady, sternly, pulling herself as erect as she could with a dragging weight of ninety pounds hanging about her neck. 'Is this the usual way you say good morning?'

The little girl dropped to her toes, and danced lightly up and down.

'No, only when I love folks so I just can't help it! I saw you from my window, Aunt Polly, and I got to thinking how you were my really truly aunt; and you looked so good I just had to come down and hug you!'

Miss Polly attempted a frown – with not her usual success.

**1 a** What type of personality does Pollyanna have?

⬜ quiet and calm ⬜ excitable and energetic

**abc** 'Remonstrated' means 'complaining in a disapproving way'.

**b** Find and copy **three** words or phrases that suggest this.

1 _____

2 _____

3 _____

**4** marks

**2 a** How does Pollyanna get ready to go outside? Tick **one** box.

⬜ slowly and calmly ⬜ quietly and nervously ⬜ quickly and excitedly

**b** How do you know this? Write your answer below.

_____

**2** marks

**3 a** In which part of the house is Pollyanna's room? Write your answer below.

_____

**b** How do you know this? Write your answer below.

_____

**2** marks

**4** Is each of the statements below true or false? Circle your answers.

Aunt Polly is gardening. true / false

Pollyanna hugs Aunt Polly around the waist. true / false

Pollyanna is happy when she greets her Aunt Polly. true / false

**3** marks

5   What does the sentence below suggest about Aunt Polly's feelings?

'PollyANNA!' remonstrated the lady, sternly, pulling herself as erect as she could.

**1 mark**

_____

6   **a**   Is the statement below true or false? Tick **one** box.

Pollyanna hugs her aunt so enthusiastically, her feet leave the ground.

☐ true          ☐ false

**b**   Find and copy **two** phrases from the text that tell you this.

1   _____

**3 marks**

2   _____

7   Aunt Polly asks Pollyanna, 'Is this the usual way you say good morning?' What does this suggest about their relationship? Tick **one** box.

☐ Aunt Polly does not know Pollyanna very well.

☐ Pollyanna is shy of Aunt Polly.

**1 mark**

☐ Pollyanna is very excited to be staying with Aunt Polly.

8   What does the phrase 'danced lightly on her toes' suggest about how Pollyanna was feeling? Write your answer below.

**1 mark**

_____

_____

9   **a**   Which of these statements best describes Aunt Polly? Tick **one** box.

☐ She doesn't care about Pollyanna at all.

☐ She is usually very stern and strict.

☐ She is always very happy to see Pollyanna.

**b**   How do you know this? Write your answer below.

**2 marks**

_____

_____

### Time to reflect

**Mark your test out of 19. How did you do?**

Check your answers in the back of the book. If any of your answers are incorrect, go to practice section 10 in Practice Book 1 to revise this topic.

# 20 Summarising

In this test you will practise summarising texts and identifying key information.

**(10)**

*This text is about the Paralympic Games.*

The Paralympic Games take place every four years and are the second largest international sporting event in the world – only the Olympic Games are larger. In the 2016 Paralympic Games, more than 4000 athletes from nearly 200 nations took part.

Paralympic athletes with a range of disabilities compete in more than 20 different sports. Many events, such as swimming, athletics and cycling, are very similar to those in the Olympic Games. However, other events have been adapted to suit the athletes' abilities. For example, athletes with mobility issues can take part in wheelchair rugby, tennis and fencing. In the 5-a-side football event, sometimes known as blind football, the ball is fitted with a device that makes a sound so that players with visual impairments can track its movements.

The Paralympics are coordinated by the International Paralympic Committee, which was founded in 1989. However, the event has its origins in the UK in 1948. Following World War II, there were many injured war veterans. Dr Ludwig Guttmann of Stoke Mandeville Hospital in Buckinghamshire recognised the importance of sport as part of their rehabilitation. He organised the first Stoke Mandeville Games in 1948, in which 16 injured servicemen and women took part. This competition evolved over many years to become the Paralympic Games.

**1** What is the main topic of this text? Tick **one** box.

◯ athletes with disabilities

◯ Dr Ludwig Guttman

◯ the Paralympic Games

**1 mark**

**2** What is the main point in the **first paragraph** of the text? Tick **one** box.

◯ Many athletes take part in the Paralympics.

◯ Many countries take part in the Paralympics.

◯ The Paralympics are a huge sporting event.

**1 mark**

**3** What is the **second paragraph** of the text about? Select **one** answer.

◯ paralympic world records

◯ blind football

◯ the events at the Paralympic Games

**1 mark**

**4** What are the events at the Paralympic Games like? Tick **one** box.

◯ Some events are very similar to those in the Olympic Games and others are adapted.

◯ The events are more challenging than in the Olympic Games.

◯ Only athletes in wheelchairs can compete in the events.

**1 mark**

**5** What is the **third paragraph** of the text about? Tick **one** box.

◻ the organisation of the Paralympic Games

◻ the history of the Paralympic Games

◻ Stoke Mandeville Hospital

**1 mark**

**6** What is the main point in the **third paragraph** of the text? Tick **one** box.

◻ The Paralympics were started in 1948 by Dr Ludwig Guttman.

◻ The Paralympics were introduced in 1948 to help the rehabilitation of injured servicemen and women.

◻ Dr Ludwig Guttman worked at Stoke Mandeville Hospital in Buckinghamshire.

**1 mark**

**7** Which of these key points would you include in a summary of the text? Tick **three** boxes.

◻ the size and importance of the Paralympic Games

◻ when the Paralympics take place

◻ the kinds of events that are included in the Paralympic Games

◻ which events are similar to the Olympic Games

◻ which events are adapted to suit the athletes' abilities

◻ who coordinates the Paralympic Games

◻ why the Paralympic Games began

**3 marks**

**8** Write a short summary of the text.

_____

_____

_____

_____

_____

**3 marks**

## Time to reflect

### Mark your test out of 12. How did you do?

Check your answers in the back of the book. If any of your answers are incorrect, go to practice section 11 in Practice Book 1 to revise this topic.

# 21 Using evidence

In this test you will practise finding and presenting information to support your answers.

(10)

*This text is from 'Alice's Adventures in Wonderland' by Lewis Carroll.*

Alice was beginning to get very tired of sitting by her sister on the bank, and of having nothing to do: once or twice she had peeped into the book her sister was reading, but it had no pictures or conversations in it, 'and what is the use of a book,' thought Alice 'without pictures or conversations?'

So she was considering in her own mind (as well as she could, for the hot day made her feel very sleepy and stupid), whether the pleasure of making a daisy-chain would be worth the trouble of getting up and picking the daisies, when suddenly a White Rabbit with pink eyes ran close by her.

There was nothing so very remarkable in that; nor did Alice think it so very much out of the way to hear the Rabbit say to itself, 'Oh dear! Oh dear! I shall be late!' (when she thought it over afterwards, it occurred to her that she ought to have wondered at this, but at the time it all seemed quite natural); but when the Rabbit actually took a watch out of its waistcoat-pocket, and looked at it, and then hurried on, Alice started to her feet, for it flashed across her mind that she had never before seen a rabbit with either a waistcoat-pocket, or a watch to take out of it, and burning with curiosity, she ran across the field after it, and fortunately was just in time to see it pop down a large rabbit-hole under the hedge.

In another moment down went Alice after it, never once considering how in the world she was to get out again.

**1  a**  Is Alice enjoying sitting by her sister? Circle **one** answer.

   yes        no

**b**  Which words tell you this? Tick **one** box.

☐ beginning to get very tired of sitting by her sister        ☐ having nothing to do        ☐ it had no pictures or conversations in it

> 2 marks

**2**  Which words tell you what Alice thinks a good book should contain? Find and copy them.

_____

> 1 mark

**3  a**  How does Alice feel as she considers whether to make a daisy chain? Tick **one** box.

☐ confused        ☐ tired        ☐ angry

**b**  How do you know this? Write your answer below.

_____

_____

> 2 marks

**4**  In your own words, explain how Alice feels before she sees the White Rabbit. Use evidence from the text in your answer.

_____

_____

_____

> 2 marks

**5**   **a**   Is Alice surprised when she first sees the White Rabbit? Circle **one** answer.

yes     no

**b**   Which words tell you this? Find and copy them.

**2**
marks

_____

**6**   In your own words, describe what Alice notices about the White Rabbit's appearance and actions. Use evidence from the text in your answer.

_____

_____

**2**
marks

_____

**7**   **a**   Why does Alice follow the White Rabbit? Tick **one** box.

☐ She is intrigued and wants to find out more about him.     ☐ She wants to help him.     ☐ She wants to get away from her sister.

**b**   Which words tell you this? Find and copy them.

**2**
marks

_____

**8**   **a**   Does Alice think carefully before she decides to follow the White Rabbit down the rabbit hole? Circle **one** answer.

yes     no

**b**   How do you know this? Write your answer below.

_____

**2**
marks

_____

**9**   In your own words, explain what kind of person you think Alice is. Use evidence from the text in your answer.

_____

_____

**2**
marks

_____

## Time to reflect

### Mark your test out of 17. How did you do?

Check your answers in the back of the book. If any of your answers are incorrect, go to practice section 12 in Practice Book 1 to revise this topic.

# 22 Understanding texts

In this test you will practise explaining the language and structure of a text.

*This text is about the artist, Vincent van Gogh.*

**(10)**

'*I dream of painting and then I paint my dream.*' *Vincent van Gogh*

Vincent van Gogh is one of the most famous and influential artists of all time. Born in the Netherlands in 1853, he produced little art in the first 27 years of his life. However, between 1880 and his death in 1890 he was prolific, creating over 2000 artworks, including more than 850 oil paintings. Famously, he once explained his methods as 'I dream of painting and then I paint my dream.'

Vincent disliked school and at the age of 14 he left. His uncle secured him a position at a firm of art dealers in Holland, then in London, then in Paris. He also worked as a teacher in England, a bookseller in Holland and a missionary in Belgium. Vincent would write to his younger brother, Theo, regularly, sometimes including little sketches. Theo encouraged him to concentrate on his drawing and offered to support him financially until he could earn a living from his art. Theo did so for the rest of Vincent's life.

Throughout his later life, Vincent suffered from poor mental health and struggled to settle in any one place, just as he had struggled to settle in any one occupation. In 1881, he moved back to the Netherlands, then to Belgium, back to the Netherlands and then, in 1886, to France.

In the south of France, Vincent shared a house with another artist, Paul Gaugin. They had very different views on art. One particularly ferocious argument ended in a fight, which resulted in Vincent severing part of his own left ear.

Throughout this time, Vincent sent his paintings to his brother, Theo, who worked as an art dealer in Paris. Vincent continued to develop his unique painting style but, despite Theo's unwavering belief in his brother's art, very few of his paintings were sold in his lifetime. Vincent died in 1890. His work has grown in popularity ever since and, though his paintings rarely come up for sale at auction, they often sell for enormous sums. His *Portrait of Dr Gachet* was sold for a record-breaking $82.5 million in 1990.

**1  a** What do we call the text in speech marks at the start of the text? Tick **one** box.

◻ an interview ◻ a quotation ◻ a poem

**b** Why has the writer used it here?

_____

**2 marks**

**2** In what tense is most of the text written? Write your answer. _____

**1 mark**

**3** Explain in your own words why the writer uses a new paragraph for the section beginning 'Vincent disliked school'.

_____

**1 mark**

**4** Find and copy **two** words in the text that mean 'job'.

1 _____  2 _____

**2 marks**

**5** What does the phrase 'he was prolific' mean? Tick **one** box.

◻ Vincent produced a small number of paintings.    ◻ Vincent was too ill to produce paintings.

◻ Vincent produced a large number of paintings.    ◻ Vincent took a very long time to produce each painting.

**1 mark**

**6  a**  How did Vincent get money when he worked as an artist? Write your answer below.

_____

**b**  Which phrase tells you this? Find and copy it.

`2 marks`

_____

`1 mark`

**7**  What type of text is this? Tick **one** box.

☐ a story       ☐ an article giving the writer's opinion       ☐ an instructional text       ☐ an informative text

**8  a**  From your reading of the text, is the statement below true or false? Tick **one** box.

Theo always thought that Vincent was a great artist.

☐ true              ☐ false

**b**  Which phrase tells you this? Find and copy it.

`2 marks`

_____

**9**  Is the clause below written in the active or passive voice? Write your answer below.

his _Portrait of Dr Gachet_ was sold for a record-breaking $82.5 million in 1990.

`1 mark`

_____

**10**  Find and copy **two** words in the text that show Vincent's later life was a difficult time for him.

`2 marks`

1 _____     2 _____

**11**  What does the word 'ferocious' mean? Write your answer below.

`1 mark`

_____

**12  a**  From your reading of the text, is the statement below true or false? Tick **one** box.

No other artist painted in the way that van Gogh did.

☐ true              ☐ false

**b**  Which phrase tells you this? Find and copy it.

`2 marks`

_____

## Time to reflect

### Mark your test out of 18. How did you do?

Check your answers in the back of the book. If any of your answers are incorrect, go to practice section 10 in Practice Book 2 to revise this topic.

# 23 Explaining texts

In this test you will practise identifying a writer's choices and explaining their effect on the reader.

*This text is about how doctors treated disease in the medieval period from the 5th to the 15th century.*

**10**

## Medieval medicine

Medieval doctors had little idea of what caused disease. Much medicine was based on a theory from the ancient Greeks, who believed that a healthy body had four 'humours' (or substances) in perfect balance: phlegm, black bile, yellow bile and blood. Ill health was caused by these humours becoming unbalanced. A diagnosis involved examining a sample of the patient's urine to identify which humour was out of balance. Treatments included:

- giving a drink to make the patient vomit and so rid their body of impurity
- applying blood-sucking creatures called leeches to release the patient's blood
- drilling a hole in the patient's skull, known as trepanning, to release pressure or evil spirits.

Simple herbal medicines were also used, often made by the patient or their family. More complex remedies could be purchased from the local apothecary, similar to a modern pharmacist. They may seem strange to us, but many medieval remedies were effective. For example, rubbing the slime from a snail on a burn was believed to heal the wound. Unlikely though it sounds, scientists in the 21st century have discovered that snail slime has antiseptic, anaesthetic and antibiotic properties, and can reduce inflammation.

However, not all remedies were so effective. For a throat infection, one medieval recipe suggests rubbing the patient's neck with grease from a cooked cat that had been stuffed with bear fat, hedgehog fat and various herbs. There is no evidence that this would have had any effect whatsoever. When an epidemic of the bubonic plague, known as the Black Death, swept through Europe between 1346 and 1353, doctors were helpless to prevent it from spreading. It has been estimated that approximately 60 per cent of the population, 50 million people, died of the disease.

**1    a**    Is the style of this text formal or informal? Write your answer below.

_____

    **b**    Why do you think it is written in this style? Tick **one** box.

☐ It is about the past.                  ☐ It is a factual account.

☐ It is about an important subject.     ☐ It is a humorous account.

**2**    marks

**2**    Find and copy a phrase in the text that tells you medieval medicine was based on very old ideas.

_____

**1**    mark

**3**    Find and copy a verb in the text that means 'to inspect in close detail'.

_____

**1**    mark

**4**    What does 'theory' mean? Write your answer below.

_____

**1**    mark

**5**    Explain in your own words why the writer has used bullet points in the text.

_____

_____

**1**    mark

**6 a** From your reading of the text, is the statement below true or false? Tick **one** box.

No medieval medicine had any effect on illnesses.

☐ true                    ☐ false

**b** Which words tells you this? Find and copy them.

**2 marks**

_____

**7** What does 'inflammation' mean? Tick **one** box.

☐ likely to catch fire    ☐ a small break in a bone    ☐ redness or swelling    ☐ losing your temper

**1 mark**

**8** Why does the writer give a detailed description of a medieval cure for a throat infection?

**1 mark**

_____

_____

**9** Why is the last paragraph an effective way for the writer to end the text? Tick **one** box.

☐ It shows how the lack of medical knowledge had an impact on people.

☐ It makes the reader feel sorry for medieval doctors.

☐ It makes the reader want to find out more about medieval medicine.

☐ It shows the reader how dangerous the bubonic plague was.

**1 mark**

**10** What does 'epidemic' mean? Tick **one** box.

☐ a very unpleasant disease

☐ an outbreak of disease affecting many people

☐ a kind of medicine used to treat the plague

☐ a kind of storm

**1 mark**

**11 a** From your reading of the text, is the statement below true or false? Tick **one** box.

The Black Death spread quickly throughout Europe.

☐ true                    ☐ false

**b** Which word tells you this? Find and copy it.

**2 marks**

_____

**12** Find and copy a phrase that tells you there was no way to stop the Black Death.

**1 mark**

_____

### Time to reflect

**Mark your test out of 15. How did you do?**

Check your answers in the back of the book. If any of your answers are incorrect, go to practice section 11 in Practice Book 2 to revise this topic.

# 24 Giving your opinion

In this test you will practise giving your own opinion about situations and characters in an extract from a short story.

*This text is from a short story called 'The Thieves Who Couldn't Stop Sneezing' by Thomas Hardy. Thieves have dragged a boy named Hubert from his horse, tied his hands and robbed him. As he is walking home in the dark, Hubert sees a large house and decides to ask for help.*

**10**

All was silent; but the door stood wide open, it being from this door that the light shone which had attracted him. On entering he found himself in a vast apartment arranged as a dining-hall, and brilliantly illuminated. But what drew his attention most was the large table in the midst of the hall, upon which was spread a sumptuous supper, as yet untouched. Chairs were placed around, and it appeared as if something had occurred to interrupt the meal just at the time when all were ready to begin.

Even had Hubert been so inclined, he could not have eaten in his helpless state, unless by dipping his mouth into the dishes, like a pig or cow. He wished first to obtain assistance; and was about to penetrate further into the house for that purpose when he heard hasty footsteps in the porch and the words, 'Be quick!' uttered in the deep voice which had reached him when he was dragged from the horse. There was only just time for him to dart under the table before three men entered the dining-hall.

'Now, then,' said the first – the man with the deep voice – 'let us hide ourselves. They will all be back again in a minute. That was a good trick to get them out of the house – eh?'

'Yes. You well imitated the cries of a man in distress,' said the second.

'Excellently,' said the third.

'But they will soon find out that it was a false alarm. Come, where shall we hide? It must be some place we can stay in for two or three hours, till all are in bed and asleep. Ah! I have it. Come this way! I have learnt that the further closet is not opened once in a twelvemonth; it will serve our purpose exactly.'

The speaker advanced into a corridor which led from the hall. Creeping a little farther forward, Hubert could discern that the closet stood at the end, facing the dining-hall. The thieves entered it, and closed the door. Hardly breathing, Hubert glided forward, to learn a little more of their intention.

**abc** 'Sumptuous' means 'splendid and luxurious'.

**1** What attracted Hubert's attention to the large house as he walked in the darkness?

☐ It was a very large house.

☐ He saw a light in the window.

☐ He saw the light from the open door.

☐ He was carrying a lantern.

**1** mark

**2** Find and copy a phrase that tells you that the owners of the house are wealthy.

_____

**1** mark

**3 a** Find and copy a phrase that describes Hubert's feelings as he stands in the dining hall.

_____

**b** Explain what this phrase tells you about how he feels.

_____

_____

_____

**2** marks

**4** The writer says that Hubert 'wished first to obtain assistance' before he could think about eating any food. What impression does this create of Hubert? Tick **one** box.

☐ He is not hungry.

☐ He is very polite and will not help himself to food.

☐ He is desperate for help.

☐ He is scared of the dark.

**5** The writer says that 'it appeared as if something had occurred to interrupt the meal just at the time when all were ready to begin.' Find and copy a phrase that explains why it looked as if the meal had been interrupted.

_____

**6** Find and copy a phrase that suggests the three men who enter the house are the thieves that attacked Hubert.

_____

**7** The writer describes how Hubert had 'to dart under the table' when the thieves came in. Why is this an effective description of his movement?

_____

**8 a** How do the thieves feel about the trick they have played on the owners of the house? Tick **one** box.

☐ They are pleased.

☐ They are angry that it did not work.

☐ They are worried that someone may have seen them.

**b** Which words tell you this? Find and copy them.

_____

**9** What does the phrase 'to learn a little more of their intention' mean? Tick **one** box.

☐ To see what the robbers look like

☐ To see if they are the same men that stole Hubert's horse

☐ To find out what they are planning to do

☐ To find out when the owners of the house will return

**10** Explain in your own words how Hubert feels as he hides under the table. Why do you think this?

_____

_____

_____

### Time to reflect

**Mark your test out of 13. How did you do?**

Check your answers in the back of the book. If any of your answers are incorrect, go to practice section 12 in Practice Book 2 to revise this topic.

# 25 Explaining poetry

In this test you will practise explaining the language choices in a poem, and give your own response to it.

*This is an extract from the poem 'The Rime of the Ancient Mariner' by Samuel Taylor Coleridge. It is about a ship on a voyage. In this section, the ship cannot move because there is no wind to fill its sails.*

**10**

## The Rime of the Ancient Mariner

1.  Down dropt the breeze, the sails dropt down,
    'Twas sad as sad could be;
    And we did speak only to break
    The silence of the sea!

2.  All in a hot and copper sky,
    The bloody Sun, at noon,
    Right up above the mast did stand,
    No bigger than the Moon.

3.  Day after day, day after day,
    We stuck, nor breath nor motion;
    As idle as a painted ship
    Upon a painted ocean.

4.  Water, water, every where,
    And all the boards did shrink;
    Water, water, every where,
    Nor any drop to drink.

**abc** The ship is made of wooden boards. In the heat of the sun the boards dry out and shrink.

**1 a** Find and copy the phrase in the first verse that tells you that the sea was calm.

_____

**b** Which literary device is this? Tick **one** box.

☐ simile ☐ personification

☐ alliteration ☐ metaphor

**2** **marks**

**2 a** The writer says the ship was 'as idle as a painted ship'. What does the word 'idle' mean here? Write your answer below.

_____

**1** **mark**

**3** What does the writer mean by 'No bigger than the Moon'? Tick **one** box.

☐ The ship is as big as the moon. ☐ The ship is smaller than the moon.

☐ The sun appears to be very small. ☐ The sun is invisible because the sky is cloudy.

**1** **mark**

**4 a** Find and copy a metaphor about the sky.

_____

**b** Explain how this helps the reader to picture the sky.

_____

_____

_____

**2** **marks**

**5**　**a**　Which phrase in the third verse tells you that there was no wind? Find and copy it.

_____

**b**　Which literary device is this? Tick **one** box.

☐ simile ☐ personification

☐ alliteration ☐ metaphor

2
marks

**6**　**a**　Find and copy an example of a simile in the poem.

_____

_____

**b**　Explain what the effect of this is.

_____

_____

2
marks

**7**　What does the writer mean by 'Water, water, every where, / Nor any drop to drink.'? Tick **one** box.

☐ The people on the ship have nothing but water to drink.

☐ The ship is surrounded by sea water but the people on the ship have no fresh water to drink.

☐ There is more water in the sea than anyone could ever possibly drink.

☐ The people on the ship have nothing to do because the ship is not moving.

1
mark

**8**　Explain in your own words what the last verse makes you think or feel about the sea, and why.

_____

_____

_____

2
marks

**Time to reflect**

**Mark your test out of 13. How did you do?**

Check your answers in the back of the book. If any of your answers are incorrect, go to practice section 13 in Practice Book 2 to revise this topic.

# 26 Writing fiction and non-fiction

This page gives you a selection of questions that you can use to practise writing. Answer questions 1 and 2 then choose one of the bullet points from the lists below. You should spend about 30 minutes planning and answering each writing question.

1   Draw lines to match each part of a story with what should happen.

beginning                    a satisfying conclusion

middle                       to set the scene

ending                       the main event happens

2   Draw lines to match each part of a non-fiction text with what should happen.

introduction                 summarises the main points

middle                       two or three main points

conclusion                   provides an outline

## Fiction

- Write a story about an animal.

- Complete the story.

  I knew something was wrong the minute I opened my eyes.

- Write a story using one of the titles below.

  Mistaken Identity

  Freedom

- Write a story about a mysterious object.

- Write a story set in a park.

## Non-fiction

- Write a newspaper article about a fundraising event.

- Write a letter to your head teacher persuading them to let your class go on a school trip.

- Write an essay with the title 'My dream holiday'.

- Complete the essay.

  It's important to learn about lots of different things at school, but my favourite subject is definitely...

- Write a newspaper article about the benefits of the internet.

### Time to reflect

**How did you do?**

Read your writing carefully, using the checklist in the answers to assess how successful your writing is. Tick each feature you have achieved, and note others as targets for future writing. You could also ask a friend or family member to read it. If you think you could improve your fiction writing, go to practice section 13 in Practice Book 1. If you could improve your non-fiction writing, go to practice section 14 in Practice Book 2.

# Answers

## Grammar and punctuation

### 1 Parts of speech

1. (went)
2. hot, **slowly**
3. (love) (watch)
4. to express how likely or necessary something is
5. (box)
6. Example: Swans are **beautiful** because they swim so **gracefully**.
7. (silly)
8. modal verb
9. adverbial phrase
10. Example: Because electricity is very dangerous, **you should be careful when using electrical equipment**.
11. Example: Pigs are **incredibly intelligent**.
12. false
13. my hiding place, a tall, dark, shadowy figure
14. Example: **Long, boring journeys** are never very enjoyable.
15. extremely naughty
16. small, blue, smelly

You could choose any appropriate adverb that describes how the traffic was moving.

You could choose any appropriate adjective to describe a swan and any appropriate adverb to describe how they swim.

Although 'silly' ends in ly, it is an adjective, not an adverb.

An adverbial phrase is a group of words that gives more information about a verb by describing how, when or where it happens. This phrase expresses when an action takes place.

Some other modal verbs are: 'must', 'might' and 'may'.

An adjectival phrase is a group of words that gives more information about a noun or pronoun.

### 2 Tenses

1. (kicked) (smashed)
2. past
3. **a** bought  **b** am saving  **c** will buy
4. **a** is called  **b** went  **c** am going
5. have visited, has finished, have arrived
6. Look for a form of the verb 'to be' plus main verbs ending in –ing.
7. (am taking)
8. Kam has tried on a new pair of trainers and has decided to buy them.
9. I am waiting for a bus. → present progressive

   I waited thirty minutes for a bus. → simple past

   I have waited ages for a bus. → present perfect
10. Example: I always **do** the same thing every day. When I **come** home, I always **complete** my homework straight away. When I **have finished** all of my homework, I **am allowed** to watch television.
11. I am often late for school.
12. I will have overcome my fear of heights.

The adverbials 'last week', 'at the moment' and 'as soon as I have saved enough' give a clue to the correct tense.

The present progressive tense is formed using the verb 'to be' and a main verb ending in -**ing**.

The present perfect tense is formed using the verb 'to have' and a main verb in the past tense.

You can give any four suitable verbs in the present tense, and one in the present perfect tense.

The future perfect tense is expressed using 'will', 'shall' or 'going to' plus 'have'.

### 3 Common punctuation marks

1. We
2. (2)
3. last, april, tenerife, it, i

'London' is a proper noun, so it needs a capital letter.

**4** false

**5** Where are your socks Rafiq?

**6** It has been raining for hours.

> The first option is missing a question mark. The third option needs a full stop, not a question mark. The fourth option is missing a full stop.

**7** true

**8** Hundreds of animal species are endangered, mainly due to the activities of humans.

> The second option incorrectly joins two sentences with a comma. The third option incorrectly separates two clauses with a full stop. The fourth option is missing a full stop.

**9** Being a successful athlete takes great skill, hard work, a lot of determination and a huge amount of time.

**10** Example: My three favourite pizza toppings are **cheese, ham and pineapple**.

**11** Steph got up at 7 am, washed her face, cleaned her teeth, went downstairs and ate her breakfast.

**12**

> 'Sunday' is a proper noun, so it needs a capital letter.

## 4 Sentences

**1** subject → the person or thing doing the action

verb → the action described in the sentence

object → the person or thing that has the action done to it

**2** subject → the police, verb → chased, object → the burglar

> The verb form must always agree with the subject.

**3** **a** <u>were</u>  **b** <u>ring</u>  **c** <u>was</u>

**4** **a** <u>live</u>  **b** <u>cheers</u>  **c** <u>knows</u>

> Notice that there is only one crowd, so this verb is singular.

**5** I try not to eat too many of them.

**6** Dinner was cooked by my brother and, surprisingly, it was delicious.

> The object becomes the subject in the passive voice.

**7** **a** First prize was won by me.

**b** A total of six hundred pounds was raised by the sponsored swim.

> Relative clauses add information to nouns. They are linked to the noun by a relative pronoun.

**8** **a** <u>that</u>  **b** <u>whose</u>  **c** <u>who</u>

**9** She loved the present **that I gave her**.

> A subordinate clause begins with a subordinating conjunction, such as 'when', 'because', 'although' or 'if'. This shows how the subordinate clause links to the main clause.

**10** **a** <u>Because we left him on his own</u>

**b** <u>when she came home</u>

**c** <u>if he does it again</u>

**11** Example: I was terrified because I had to make a speech in front of the whole class.

> 'When I had to make a speech in front of the whole class, I was terrified.' is also acceptable.

**12.** The relative pronoun is used incorrectly.

> It should say: 'The kitchen worktop was covered in puddles of cake mixture **that** were dripping onto the floor.'

## 5 Parenthesis

**1** King Harold was defeated at the Battle of Hastings (which famously took place in 1066).

**2** **a** <u>(I was probably about three)</u>

**b** <u>the largest country in Africa</u>

**3** When my grandparents first went to Spain (long before it was a popular holiday destination) they camped in a farmer's field.

> The answer could use either brackets or commas around the additional information.

**4** The final was one of the most exciting and enjoyable matches that I have played in (even though we lost).

**5** Example: My pen pal (whose name is Henri) lives in France.

> 'My pen pal (who lives in France) is called Henri.' is also acceptable.

**6** I do my homework, which we get almost every day, as soon as I get home from school.

> Try reading the sentence aloud, leaving different parts out. The part you can leave out without affecting the sense of the sentence is parenthesis.

**7** Example: My aunt (who is my father's sister) lives in Scotland.

**8** Example: Roald Dahl (the popular children's author) wrote many of his books in his garden shed.

**9** ②

**10** On my birthday, Mum made me chocolate cake (which is my favourite) and a huge pizza smothered in cheese.

**11** After breakfast, but before I go to school, I always do ten minutes' piano practice.

**12** Example: My dog (a terrier called Brian) ate my homework.

## 6 Prepositions

**1** <u>outside</u>

**2** **a** <u>through</u>     **b** direction

**3** under

**4** past

**5** in

**6** **a** <u>for</u>     **b** time

**7** **a** before     **b** time

**8** <u>by</u>

**9** Example: I get to school by car.

**10** out

**11** <u>for swimming</u>

**12** **a** before     **b** time

## 7 Conjunctions

**1** We played brilliantly for ninety minutes but did not score a goal.

**2** and

**3** **a** <u>until</u>     **b** subordinating

**4** true

**5** false

**6** **a** because     **b** subordinating

**7** but

**8** Cheetahs can run very fast but they tire very quickly.

**9** because

**10** **a** and     **b** coordinating

**11** Beat the butter and sugar until you have a smooth paste.

**12** if

**13** Example: The meal looked delicious **but I was too full to eat any of it**.

**14** Example: I did all the washing up **before I ate any cake**.

## 8 Direct speech

**1** false

**2** 'I'm making spaghetti tomorrow,' said Dimitri.

**3** ④

**4** 'You must put your hand up and wait patiently,' said Ms Choudhuri, 'if you want to answer a question.'

**5** 'How many have you got?' asked Jamie. // 'I've got three,' said Aled. // 'And I've got four,' laughed Adi, 'so I win.'

**6** '<u>there</u> is only one rule in this club,' said the coach, 'and it's that you should try your hardest and do your best at all times.'

'<u>what</u> if my best is not very good?' asked Marta.

The answer could use brackets, commas or dashes around the additional information.

There should be a comma at the start of the parenthesis, before 'which'.

A pair of dashes or brackets is also acceptable.

The answer could use brackets, commas or dashes around the additional information.

The preposition 'outside' indicates where the car was parked.

The word 'through' indicates movement, so it is a preposition of direction.

'For' can be a preposition of time or cause. Here it indicates how much time has passed.

In this sentence, the preposition 'by' indicates how something was done, so it is a preposition of cause.

Coordinating conjunctions link two main clauses in a sentence.

Subordinating conjunctions link a main clause and a subordinate clause in a sentence.

In the second option, 'because' is a subordinating conjunction.

In the first option, 'and' is a coordinating conjunction.

This is the only answer with:
- speech marks at the start and end of the spoken words
- a punctuation mark before the closing speech marks
- a full stop at the end of the sentence.

There should be a full stop before the closing speech marks.

You should start a new paragraph each time the speaker changes.

No capital letter is needed for 'and' because it is part of the same sentence about rules.

**7** (3) — The opening speech mark in the second section of direct speech is missing.

**8** 'I looked on the internet,' said Zak, 'and found all the information that I needed.'

**9** Neil Armstrong said, 'That's one small step for man, one giant leap for mankind,' when he took his first step on the surface of the moon.

**10** (1) — There should be a comma at the end of the first section of direct speech, before the closing speech marks.

**11** 'What did you get on the test?' Charlie asked. 'I got full marks,' he added, smiling. // 'I got two wrong,' said Ben, 'but it wasn't fair because I was late.' // 'Being on time is all part of the test,' laughed Charlie.

**12** "Mum, can I have a pony?" asked Amy.
"A pony?" shrieked Mum, "Where would we keep it?"
"It could live in my room," said Amy.
"How would it get up the stairs?" asked Mum.

**13** 'I have never,' she sighed, 'in my life,' she added, 'been so disappointed.'

**14** 'I bet it's somewhere really boring,' moaned my brother, 'It usually is.' — The final section of direct speech is a new sentence, so there should be a full stop after 'moaned my brother'.

## 9 Colons, semi-colons and dashes

**1** true

**2** To make pancakes: you will need just three ingredients eggs, milk and flour. — The colon should come after 'ingredients' to introduce the list of ingredients.

**3** Many people believe dinosaurs were wiped out by a massive meteorite**;** others argue that it was due to a sharp increase in volcanic activity.

**4** I need to do this homework quickly**:** it is due in tomorrow. — A colon is used because it is introducing an explanation.

**5** To build a hedgehog restaurant, you will need: a wooden or plastic box, one with a lid is ideal; a sharp knife (and an adult to help you use it); some strong sticky tape, e.g. duct tape; and some old bricks or large stones.

**6** That film made me cry – I had to turn it off.

**7** I went home; feeling exhausted. — The second part of this sentence ('feeling exhausted') is not a main clause, so it cannot not be separated using a semi-colon.

**8** Computer games are addictive: you can spend hours playing and still want to play more.

**9** Computer games are addictive; they are designed to be.

**10** Lots of relatives came camping with us: my uncle, who loves camping; my aunt, who hates camping; and my three cousins, who are very small and annoying.

**11** The sun was shining: the breeze was warm. — There are two main clauses in this sentence, so a semi-colon should be used to separate them.

**12** There are several species that are unique to Australia: calm, gentle koalas that can sleep for 20 hours a day; energetic kangaroos that can cover 7 metres in one hop; and many, many others.

## 10 Apostrophes

**1** I **haven't** got any time to lose. — The apostrophe is positioned between **n** and **t** because the **o** in 'not' has been missed out.

**2** I would if I could but I **can't** so I **won't**.

**3** Dad put Lucas's socks in the wash.

**4** The Romans' engineering techniques were highly advanced, enabling them to build roads, tunnels, bridges and aqueducts. — 'Romans' is a plural noun, so the apostrophe is placed after the final **s**.

**5** (its) (its) — 'Its' means 'belonging to it'. 'It's' is a contraction of 'it is'.

**6** Lois's hamster loves carrots.

7 ①   ●————————————————————  **This sentence is about more than one dog, so the apostrophe should come after the s.**

8 (it's) ●

9  Elena has borrowed her friend's calculator.

10  My mum's gone to my sister's school to watch a play.   **In this sentence, 'it's' is a contraction of 'it is'.**

11 ④

12 (its)

13  My grandma's cat is very moody.

14  He **shouldn't** ask if he **doesn't** want to hear the answer.

15  It's Tom's birthday so we're having a party.

16 ④  ●————————————————————  **The apostrophe is in the wrong place in the contraction. It should be 'wasn't'.**

# Spelling

## 11 Prefixes and suffixes

1  re<u>ferr</u>ed re<u>fe</u>rence oc<u>curr</u>ence <u>diff</u>erence

2  **a** <u>hilarious</u>  **b** <u>delicious</u>  **c** <u>nutritious</u>  ●————  **The i in the suffix -ious is often silent.**

3  **dis**appear, **dis**connect, **mis**behave, **dis**honest

4  (write) (frightening) (night) (midnight) (right)   **You usually drop the final e before adding a suffix that begins with a vowel.**

5  loving, writing, believing, dancing ●

6  **a** adventurous  **b** hazardous  **c** courageous   **Keep the final e in 'courageous' because it makes the g sound soft.**
   **d** famous

7  comfort**able**, fashion**able**, invis**ible**, imposs**ible**, unbeliev**able**, sens**ible**   **If the root word is complete, you usually add -able.**

8  **ir**relevant, **im**patient, **im**mobile, **ir**resistible

9  **a** information  **b** preparation (or preparing)
   **c** donation  **d** hesitation   **You usually drop the final e before adding a suffix that begins with a vowel, such as -ation.**

10  **in**correct, **il**logical, **il**literate, **in**destructible ●

11  **a** (different)  **b** (brilliant)  **c** (assistant)
    **d** (intelligent)  **e** (pleasant)   **Usually the suffix -tial follows a consonant, and -cial follows a vowel.**

12  **a** essen**tial**  **b** spe**cial**  **c** ini**tial** ●
    **d** offi**cial**

13  **a** celebration  **b** attraction  **c** organisation
    **d** description

14  **im**perfect, **dis**interested, **in**dependent, **ir**regular, **mis**spell

## 12 Plural nouns and tricky spellings

1  embarrassed   **'Half' and 'shelf' end in f, so the plural is formed using -ves. 'Lady' and 'party' end in y so the plural is formed using -ies.**

2  **a** halves  **b** ladies  **c** shelves ●
   **d** parties

3  **a** thorough  **b** cough  **c** rough

4  **a** buckets  **b** brushes  **c** families ●   **Remember: add -es to words ending in -sh, -ch, -s, -ss, -x, -z, when forming the plural.**

5  **a** sheep  **b** feet  **c** people

6  ① ●————————————————————  **'Wishs' should be spelled 'wishes'.**

7  (quizzes)

8  **a** gentlemen  **b** babies  **c** children

9  definitely

10  **a** queen  **b** queue  **c** opaque

11  **a** (witches)  **b** (princesses)  **c** (kisses)
    **d** (splashes)

**12** ③ •————————————— 'Storys' should be 'stories'.

**13 a** argue     **b** vague     **c** plague

**14 a** necessary     **b** themselves

## 13 Silent letters

**1** orchestra

The letter **w** is usually silent when it comes before an **r**.

**2 a** What     **b** Why     **c** When

**3** I **w**rote down an answer but I think I got it **w**rong.

**4** ③ •————————————— 'Coamed' should be spelled with a silent **b**: 'combed'.

**5** My favourite subjects at sc**h**ool are c**h**emistry and tec**h**nology.

**6 a** (hours)     **b** (rhyme)     **c** (character)

**7 a** (wrestler)     **b** (knee)     **c** (muscle)

**8** knowledge

**9** The **k**night took out his s**w**ord and **k**nocked on the door of the cas**t**le.

**10** ④ •————————————— The word 'stomach' ends with a silent **h**. This is the same **ch** pattern as 'ache' and 'school'.

**11 a** crumbs     **b** doubt     **c** climbed

**12** fascinating

**13** ① •————————————— 'Seen' should be spelled with a silent **c**: 'scene'.

**14 a** (wrap)     **b** (whole)     **c** (foreign)

**15 a** scissors     **b** wrist     **c** echo •—————

                                        **a** 'Knives' would also be correct.
                                        **b** 'Knee' would also be correct.

**16** scra**t**ching, cup**b**oard, t**w**o, wa**t**ching, lis**t**ening, could, **w**hat, **k**new

## 14 Homophones and homonyms

**1** false •—————————————

Homonyms are words that are spelled the same but have different meanings.

**2 a** aloud     **b** allowed

**3 a** their     **b** there     **c** they're •—————

'They're' is a contraction of 'they are'.

**4** Example: The season that follows winter. •—————

'A metal coil' would also be correct.

**5** Example: I do not know whether I will go to the party.

     Example: The weather looks nice this morning.

**6** Example: It wasn't fair that we lost. •—————

A sentence about a fairground would also be correct.

**7 a** who's     **b** whose •—————

**8** Example: A sealed metal container, often used to store food such as soup.

'Who's' is a contraction of 'who is'.

**9 a** where     **b** wear     **c** were

**10** Example: I like to lie on the sofa watching television.

     Example: My sister told me a lie.

**11 a** past     **b** passed

**12** Example: I enjoy peace and quiet.

     Example: I often eat a piece of toast for breakfast.

**13** Example: I promise to wave goodbye when the boat sets off.

**14 a** advise     **b** licence     **c** practise •—————

The suffix **-ice** is usually used for nouns and the suffix **-ise** is usually used for verbs.

## 15 ie/ei and ough spellings

**1 a** (deceitful)     **b** (mischievous) •—————

When the sound is /ee/, use **i** before **e** except after **c**.

**2** rece**i**pt     **3** plough     **4** doughnut

**5** ④ •————————————— 'Thougtless' should be spelled 'thoughtless'.

**6 a** (shield)     **b** (chief)

**7** ce**i**ling     **8** though     **9** parties •—————

To form the plural of a word that ends with a consonant and then a **y**, drop the **y** and add **-ies**.

10 ②　　　11　believe　　12　enough

13 ④　　　14　relief　　15　galaxies

16　a　(brief)　　b　(receive)

17　trough　　18　shriek

19　Example: We drove through the countryside to the beach.

20　countries, ought　　21　③

**Q 10** 'Brort' should be spelled 'brought'.

**Q 13** The **i** and **e** should be the other way around. The correct spelling is 'achieve'.

The correct spelling is 'although'.

## 16 Tricky spellings

1　di**ct**ionary　2　**shopping**　3　tomorrow

4　biscuits　　5　diff**er**ent

6　Booking tickets for the cinema is not always necessary.

7　remember　8　③　　9　sep**a**rate

10　adding

11　a　v**e**getable　b　f**a**mily

12　hopping, skipping, running, jumping

13　real**ly**　　14　chocolate　15　addresses

16　mis**e**rable

17　a　grin**ned**　　b　drop**ped**

18　My sister started chating to me.　19　④

'Shop' has one syllable and ends in a consonant-vowel-consonant pattern, so you double the final letter before you add the suffix.

The correct spelling is 'business'.

The correct spelling is 'chatting'.

The correct spelling is 'interesting'.

# Comprehension

## 17 Locating information

1　At the door of the inn.

2　a　winter　　b　bitter, foggy, frosty

3　a　hunched　　b　startled

4　slowly approaching the narrator

5　obviously or clearly

6　a　true　　b　dreadful-looking

7　precious

8　a　He is a teenager　b　a young voice, young friend, boy

9　a　polite and friendly

　　b　Example: raising his voice in an odd sing-song voice

10　firmly and powerfully

11　because the narrator will not take him to see the captain

12　a sudden violent pull

In this context, the verb 'drawing' means 'moving'.

A vice is a tool used to clamp an object firmly in place.

The blind man says 'take me in to the captain' and 'Take me in straight or I'll break your arm' just before he hurts the narrator.

## 18 Language for effect

1　a　The sunbeam showers break and quiver

　　b　Example: The sunlight is pouring down strongly, like rain.

2　a　Like an angel

　　b　She sings as beautifully as an angel.

3　alliteration　　4　metaphor

5　alliteration and personification　6　personification

7　creaking　　8　as cold and still as a stone

The writer describes the webs as 'shivering', which is usually a human action, and uses alliteration in the two adjectives 'shredded' and 'shivering'.

'Like a pirate's treasure chest' is also acceptable.

## 19 Inference

1　a　excitable and energetic　b　Example: flew, sped, bang

2　a　quickly and excitedly　b　with rapid fingers

3　a　in the attic

The word 'rapid' suggests that Pollyanna is moving very quickly.

**b** We are told she 'made herself ready' then ran 'down the attic stairs'.

**4** ⟨true⟩ ⟨false⟩ ⟨true⟩

**5** The sentence suggests that Aunt Polly is annoyed and angry to see Pollyanna.

> Aunt Polly is inspecting a rosebush when we first see her. Pollyanna is 'hanging about' Aunt Polly's neck when she hugs her. Pollyanna is 'gurgling with delight'.

**6 a** true

**b** 1 a dragging weight of ninety pounds hanging about her neck

2 The little girl dropped to her toes

> The capital letters and exclamation mark could also suggest that Aunt Polly is surprised.

**7** Aunt Polly does not know Pollyanna very well.

**8** Pollyanna is happy and excited.

**9 a** She is always very stern and strict.

**b** The writer says that Aunt Polly 'attempted a frown' but 'with not her usual success', which suggests she frowns a lot.

> Aunt Polly's words suggest she does not know how Pollyanna usually says good morning. This could suggest this is the first morning they have spent together.

## 20 Summarising

**1** the Paralympic Games

**2** the Paralympics are a huge sporting event.

> The key point in a paragraph is often found in its first sentence.

**3** the events at the Paralympic Games

**4** Some events are very similar to those in the Olympic Games and others are adapted.

> All three phrases are relevant, but the majority of the paragraph focuses on events that are similar and adapted.

**5** The history of the Paralympic Games

**6** The Paralympics were introduced in 1948 to help the rehabilitation of injured servicemen and women.

**7** 1 the size and importance of the Paralympic Games
2. the kinds of events that are included in the Paralympic Games

3. why the Paralympic Games began

**8** Example: The Paralympic Games are a huge sporting event in which disabled athletes compete in a range of events including football, cycling and swimming. They began in 1948 to help rehabilitate injured servicemen and women.

> The summary focuses on the key points in each of the text's three paragraphs.

## 21 Using evidence

**1 a** no

**b** beginning to get very tired of sitting by her sister

**2** pictures or conversations

**3 a** tired     **b** sleepy and stupid

> This answer summarises all the important points and supports them with evidence from the text.

**4** Example: Alice is feeling tired and bored. I know this because it says she is 'very tired of sitting by her sister' and 'of having nothing to do'. She is also sleepy because it is a hot day.

**5 a** no     **b** nothing so very remarkable

> 'It all seemed quite natural' is also acceptable. These short phrases clearly show that Alice is not surprised when the White Rabbit first appears.

**6** Example: The White Rabbit has pink eyes. It is running and talking to itself. It is wearing a 'waistcoat' and takes 'a watch' out of its pocket. Finally, it disappears 'down a large rabbit-hole under the hedge'.

> This answer includes all of the important information given in the text and is supported with evidence.

**7 a** She is intrigued and wants to find out more about him

**b** burning with curiosity

**8 a** ⟨no⟩

**b** We are told that Alice follows the rabbit down the rabbit hole, 'never once considering' how she will get out again.

> You could infer that the other answers are true, but this is the most clear explanation from the evidence in the text.

**9**   Example: Alice is a brave and adventurous person. When she saw the White Rabbit, she 'started to her feet' and 'ran across the field after it'. She follows it down the rabbit hole without even 'considering how in the world she was to get out again'.

This answer uses a range of evidence from the text to answer the question.

## 22 Understanding texts

**1**   **a**   a quotation

  **b**   To introduce Vincent van Gogh's attitude to art

Speech marks can indicate dialogue or quotation in a text.

**2**   the past tense

Look at the verbs in the text to help you work out the tense.

**3**   Example: The text changes topic and time. It moves from van Gogh's achievements to his early life.

Writers should start a new paragraph when they talk about a new person, place or topic, or when the story moves forwards or backwards in time.

**4**   position; occupation

**5**   Vincent produced a large number of paintings.

**6**   **a**   His brother gave him money

  **b**   support him financially

**7**   an informative text

**8**   **a**   true       **b**   Theo's unwavering belief in Vincent's art

**9**   the passive voice

**10**   struggled, suffered

Factual accounts are usually written in a formal style. It gives the reader the impression that the text is reliable and trustworthy.

**11**   Example: extreme

**12**   **a**   true       **b**   unique painting style

## 23 Explaining texts

**1**   **a**   formal       **b**   It is a factual account.

**2**   based on a theory from the ancient Greeks

You may not know that the ancient Greeks lived a long time before the medieval period, but the word 'ancient' gives you a clue.

**3**   examining

**4**   Example: An idea that has not been proven

Look for clues around the word 'theory'. The word 'believed' suggests this was an idea which had not yet been proven.

**5**   Example: The writer uses bullet points to organise a list of information, making it clearer and easier to read.

**6**   **a**   false   **b**   many medieval remedies were effective

Look for evidence in the text that agrees or disagrees with the statement in the question.

**7**   redness or swelling

**8**   Example: This is included to create humour to entertain the reader, and to inform the reader of the strange and surprising medicines that were used in medieval times.

This is a 'why' question so think about how this section of the text might make the reader think or feel.

**9**   It shows how the lack of medical knowledge had an impact on people.

**10**   an outbreak of disease affecting many people

Look for evidence in the text that agrees or disagrees with the statement in the question. Which word in the evidence most strongly conveys the idea in the statement?

**11**   **a**   true       **b**   swept

**12**   doctors were helpless to prevent it from spreading

## 24 Giving your opinion

**1**   He saw the light from the open door.

**2**   vast apartment

**3**   **a**   Even if he had been so inclined, he could not have eaten in his helpless state

  **b**   This suggests that even if his hands were not tied, he would still feel too worried or upset to eat.

All other details in this part of the text suggest that the people in the house were ready to eat. There were chairs around the table, which was 'spread with a sumptuous supper', but none of the food had been touched.

**4**   He is desperate for help.

**5**   as yet untouched

**6**   the deep voice which had reached him when he was dragged from the horse

**7** Example: The word 'dart' suggests that Hubert had to move quickly, which shows that he was frightened. This helps to make the story tense and exciting.

**8**  **a**  They are pleased.

    **b**  For example: 'a good trick', 'You well imitated the cries of a man in distress'.

**9**  To find out what they are planning to do

**10**  Example: Hubert is nervous because the writer says he is 'hardly breathing'. He is also curious and brave because the writer says he creeps forward from his hiding place to find out what the thieves are doing.

## 25 Explaining poetry

**1**  **a**  The silence of the sea!  **b**  alliteration

**2**  still or lazy

**3**  The sun appears to be very small.

**4**  **a**  copper sky

    **b**  Example: It suggests that the sun has made the sky the colour of copper, giving it a warm, metallic, shiny quality.

**5**  **a**  nor breath  **b**  personification

**6**  **a**  As idle as a painted ship / Upon a painted ocean

    **b**  Example: It shows that the boat is completely still and lifeless, like a painting.

**7**  The ship is surrounded by sea water but the people on the ship have no fresh water to drink.

**8**  Example: It makes the sea sound dangerous, because if the wind stops you are stuck, surrounded by miles of water. It would be frightening if you did not have any water to drink.

# Composition

## 26 Writing fiction and non-fiction

**1**  beginning → to set the scene

    middle → the main event happens

    ending → a satisfying conclusion

**2**  introduction → provides an outline

    middle → two or three main points

    conclusion → summarises the main points

A good story should include: a beginning that sets the scene; a middle where an important event happens; a satisfying ending; a range of punctuation; interesting word choices; descriptive adjectives and adverbs.

A good non-fiction piece of writing should include: a clear introduction explaining what the topic is; a middle with two or three main points; a conclusion that summarises your ideas; formal language; a range of correct punctuation; non-fiction features, for example: subheadings, lists and facts.

Look closely at the part of the text where the characters' feelings are suggested. What do the words and phrases in that part of the text suggest about their feelings?

Use your answers to the earlier questions to help you form an opinion. How would you feel if you were in this situation?

Remember to state your opinion clearly then explain why you think that.

Alliteration is a sequence of words that start with the same sound. They must be next to each other or close together.

Personification is when a non-human thing is given human traits, such as breathing.

A simile is a kind of comparison. What does the comparison suggest about the thing the writer is describing?

Remember to state your opinion clearly and give reasons to explain it using clues from the poem.

You could also ask a friend or family member to read your writing and answer these questions:
- Did you enjoy the piece?
- Did the structure make sense?
- Was the language interesting?
- Was the spelling and punctuation correct?

Published by Pearson Education Limited, 80 Strand, London, WC2R 0RL.

www.pearsonschools.co.uk

Text © Pearson Education Limited 2018
Edited, typeset and produced by Elektra Media Ltd
Original illustrations © Pearson Education Limited
Illustrated by Elektra Media Ltd
Cover design by Lukas Bischoff

The right of David Grant to be identified as author of this work has been asserted by him in accordance with the
Copyright, Designs and Patents Act 1988.

First published 2018

21 20 19 18
10 9 8 7 6 5 4 3 2 1

**British Library Cataloguing in Publication Data**
A catalogue record for this book is available from the British Library

ISBN: 978 1 292 24668 0

Printed in Slovakia by Neografia

**Acknowledgements**

We would like to thank Faye Cheeseman and Steph Niland for their invaluable help in the development and trialling
of this publication.

**Note from the publisher**
Pearson has robust editorial processes, including answer and fact checks, to ensure the accuracy of the content in
this publication, and every effort is made to ensure this publication is free of errors. We are, however, only human,
and occasionally errors do occur. Pearson is not liable for any misunderstandings that arise as a result of errors in
this publication, but it is our priority to ensure that the content is accurate. If you spot an error, please do contact
us at resourcescorrections@pearson.com so we can make sure it is corrected.